GATTEGNO MATHEMATICS

Text-Book I

The Text-book Series

GATTEGNO

MATHEMATICS

TEXT-BOOK I

by

C. GATTEGNO

EDUCATIONAL SOLUTIONS
NEW YORK, N.Y. 10003

© 1970   C. Gattegno
SBN 87825 011 5

The title GATTEGNO MATHEMATICS
embodies an approach best expressed by
the phrase The Subordination of Teaching
to Learning. The programme covered in
this series envisages the use of colored
rods (ALGEBRICKS) and other books
and printed materials that are obtainable
from:

EDUCATIONAL SOLUTIONS INC.
821 Broadway, New York, N.Y. 10003

Printed in Great Britain by
Lamport Gilbert Printers Ltd.,
Wantage Road, Reading, England

CONTENTS

I

SESSIONS OF FREE PLAY

II

QUALITATIVE WORK
WITH THE RODS

Part II

QUALITATIVE WORK
WITH THE RODS

Equivalence by color and by length

1. In your set of colored rods, find all those that are the same color.

Mix all the rods together again.

Now find all the rods that are the same length.

Trains

2. Form a **train** by putting rods **end to end.**

All trains are made of more than one rod.

The smallest train will be of two rods.

Make as many trains as you wish, and name them using the color names of the rods.

Make a train of two rods **equivalent** in length to the tan rod or to the blue rod.

Can you make trains of more than two rods equivalent in length to any of the following rods:

    orange
    black
    dark green
    blue
    tan

Make as many trains as you can for each of these rods.

Patterns

3. When you find as many trains as you can equivalent to one of the rods, and you place the trains close together and **side by side,** we shall say that you have made a **pattern.**
Make a pattern for the yellow rod.

Do you have the **following** trains:
> a pink and a white
> a red and a light green
> a white and a pink
> a light green and a red
> a white and two red
> a red, a white and a red
> a light green and two white
> a white, a light green and a white
> two red and a white
> three white and a red
> five white rods.

Make patterns for some of the other rods; for the black or the blue. When you have a pattern that shows all the trains which are equivalent to any one of the rods, we shall say you have the **complete** pattern of that rod.

Make the complete pattern for the red
> the light green
> the pink
> the yellow
> the dark green rod

You may find that you have not enough rods to make the complete patterns for all of these other rods. If you can only make **incomplete** patterns, **think** of the trains you need to make the patterns complete.

5

4. Which are the rods whose pattern **includes** one of these trains:

red, white, red, white, red;
red, yellow, white;
light green, red, white;
light green, red, red, light green;
white, light green, pink.

Make your own trains and ask your neighbour to guess the rod or rods, which when put end to end, are equivalent to them.

Smaller, bigger

5. If you put a red rod and an orange rod end to end, are they **bigger** or **smaller** than a blue rod?

a tan?
a black?
an orange?
an orange and a white?
an orange and a light green?

6. If you take a pink rod, can you find a rod that is **equal** to it?
One that is smaller?
One that is bigger?
Two rods which end to end are equal to it?
Or smaller?
Or bigger?
Try this with the yellow rod, and then all the other colors.

7. If you take a red rod and then a yellow one, can you find which rod you need to place

end to end with the red one to make the same length as the yellow one?

Do it again with two other rods and find the missing one.

8. Put two rods end to end.

Now take one that is smaller than the length you have just made and find the rod which you must put end to end with it to make the same length as the others.

Do it again choosing different rods.

9. If we now mix four rods from one of the patterns you have just made, which must we put with which to make two equal lengths?

Mix them again and put any two end to end.

What happens then?

Try again, exchanging your four rods for those of a neighbour who has been doing a similar thing.

Staircase

10. Now let us take one rod of each color and make a **staircase.**

Which rod is the biggest?

Which is the smallest?

Which comes before the biggest?

Which comes after the smallest?

Move up the staircase saying the colors of the rods you meet.

Move down, saying the colors of the rods you meet.

Can you do the same thing with your eyes shut, starting with the white rod?

Now do it starting with the orange rod.

7

Now you will know the colors of the rods in a **sequence**.

11. Let us look at our staircase. Which rods do we need if we want to make every step **level** with the orange rod?
Find them and put them in their places.

12. Now take them away and leave the staircase as it was before.
Can you **tell** which rod is needed for the blue?
    for the yellow?
    for the light green?

Complementaries

13. Take an orange rod and put a black rod side by side with it.
Which rod do you need to put end to end with the black to make the length of the orange?
Keep the orange rod, and now put a dark green rod side by side with it.
Which do you need to put with the dark green to make the length of the orange?
Find what you need to make the length of the orange if you start with

    a yellow rod
    a blue rod
    a red rod
    a tan rod
    a light green rod
    a pink rod

The rods you find will be called the **complement** in the orange of the ones given to you.

14. Put a black rod and a light green end to end. Which rod is equivalent in length to that train?

Which do we need for the pink and dark green train?

for the blue and white?
for the red and tan?
for the dark green and pink?
for the white and blue?
for the tan and red?

15. Do the same thing again with the red and the black, with the white and the tan, with the light green and the dark green, and with the yellow and the pink.

16. With a tan and a yellow rod end to end, find which other rods end to end give the same length.

17. Take any **pair** of rods, put them end to end, and find as many pairs of rods as possible, which, end to end, give the same length. Now put more than two rods end to end and then make equal lengths with other rods.

18. Take any rod, then another smaller one. Find which rod must be put with the smaller one to make the length of the longer one, and do this exercise

(1) using rods;
(2) looking at the rods, and showing the rod you need;
(3) only hearing the names of the rods and saying which rod is needed.

19. Do this with rods of each of the colors. Now do it starting with a length made of two rods end to end.

Trains of one color

20. Try to form the length of any one rod by using only red rods.
Can you always do it?
And with light green rods only. Can you always do it?
And with pink rods only.
With yellow rods only.

21. Which rods can be covered by using only red rods?
by using only light green ones?
by using only pink ones?
by using only yellow ones?

22. Which rod do you need to make a train of the length of the rod you started with when you can't do it with a train made only of red ones?
When you can't do it with the green ones?

23. Begin by making a train of **several** red rods.
Take some rods of one other color and make a train which you can put side by side with the red train, starting at one end of the red train.
See if any of the rods you are using in this train ends at the same place as one of the rods in the red train.

24. Make trains using only dark green rods and only black rods.
Can they be the same length?

25. Make trains that are all tan and all orange.
Can they be the same length?

26. Begin by making a train of red rods end to end on a straight line. Take a few rods of each of the other colors and put them, **in turn,** against the train starting at one end. You thus get several trains side by side each of one color. Which rods end at the end of a red rod in the various trains?
Which do not?

27. Make a train of light green rods and put side by side with this, some **one color** trains made of other rods, so that you have several trains.
Which trains have a rod which ends at the end of one of the **light green** rods?
Which do not?

28. Do the same, starting with a train of pink rods.
And then starting with a train of yellow rods.

29. Make trains with rods of only one color: all red, all light green, all pink, and put them one against the other with one end level. Can you make trains of the same length if one is red, and the other pink?

if one is red and the other light green?
if one is light green and the other pink?

30. Now make three trains side by side, a red, a light green and a pink train.
Do the three trains make the same length?
Do this again to make three trains of one color, all of which are the same length, but not using the same three colors you have just used.

Transformations

31. Let the tan rod be considered as a train of one color with one coach only, and put another train next to it made of a red and two light green rods.
Are the trains the same length?
Put the red rod between the two green ones.
Take away the red one and push one green rod up to the other. Which rod do you need to make the second train the same length as the tan?

32. Let the orange rod be one train and make another with a yellow, a light green and a red.
Is it the same length as the orange?
If you take away the green rod and push one of the rods that are left up to the other, either to the **right** or the **left,** which rod will you need to make the second train the same length as the orange?

33. Make these patterns:
(a) take a blue rod; take two white rods and put them side by side with the blue rod, one at each end.

Which rod is needed to fill the space?
Which rod is needed to fill the space if you use red rods instead of white ones?
if you use light green?
if you use pink?

(b)   take a blue rod; in the same places as before put any two rods which together are smaller than the blue.
Which rod is needed to fill the space between them when you have used

a white and a red?	a red and a pink?
a white and a black?	a yellow and a red?
a white and a light green?	a pink and a light green?

34.   Do this again starting with a black rod;
        with a tan rod;
        with an orange rod;

35.   Can you say, **without doing it,** which rods will be needed to fill the space in these patterns:

(a)   a dark green rod with two white ones next to it, one at each end?
        a dark green with one white and one red?

(b)   a black rod with a red and a light green rod next to it at each of the ends?
        a black rod with two red ones?
        a black rod with two light green ones?
Do this first when you have the rods in front of you, and again when you are asked and only hear the names of the rods.

13

36. Take any one of the three biggest rods. Reading the names here, and using your eyes, and not touching the rods, find which rods would fill the space if we put a red rod at each end, or

> a white at one end and a red at the other,
> a white at one end and a yellow at the other,
> a light green at each end.

Try more **exercises** in this way, using your own **inventions.**

Odd and even lengths

37. The rods whose length can be formed by trains of one white rod followed by two of another color or two more white rods, we shall call **odd.**

The other rods we shall call **even.**

By making trains, find all the odd lengths in your set.

Find which are the even ones.

38. If we form a train of three rods with a white rod in the middle and two rods of another colour, do we form a length that is odd or even? Form more trains in this way with a white in the middle, and using for the other two rods a **pair** from each of the other colors.

Can the lengths of all the rods in your set be made in this way?

39. Put two odd lengths end to end. Is the new length odd?

Put two even lengths end to end. Is the new length even?

What can we say if we put an odd length and an even length end to end?

III

LITERAL WORK

Part III

LITERAL WORK

The signs for addition, for difference and for equivalence

1. If we **compare** a black rod with an orange rod, we can see by how much the orange rod is bigger.

Which rod will you put end to end with the black to make a train of a length equivalent to that of the orange?

The length of the rod which fits can be called the **difference** between the length of the black and that of the orange.

Will you find the rod whose length is the difference between those of

the blue and the pink.
the dark green and the red.
the light green and the dark green.
the red and the white.

2. Instead of using the names of the colors of the rods, let us use the following letters:

w for white
r for red
g for light green
p for pink
y for yellow
d for dark green

b for black
t for tan or brown
B for blue
o for orange.

When we wish to write that two rods are end to end we put the sign $+$, and read it **plus**.

$w+r$ tells us that the white rod and the red rod are end to end.

Let us write $-$ between two letters when we wish to show that we have two lengths, and we are measuring the difference between them. We shall read this sign **minus**.

$o-w$ tells us we want the rod whose length is the difference between the lengths of the orange and the white rods.

You can find that B is equivalent to $o-w$.

What is equivalent to $y-r$?

Let us put $=$ whenever we would say is **equivalent** to.

For what you have just done you could write:

$$g=y-r.$$

Write down some differences and show the answers in this way.

3. Make a staircase using one rod of each of the different colors.

Find which rod measures the difference between any two **successive** rods in the staircase.

$o=B+w$, tells us that the orange rod is bigger than the blue rod, by the length of the white rod.

What do we understand from

$$t=b+w$$
$$y=p+w$$

$$g= r+w$$
$$r=w+w?$$

When we put down these signs for what we are doing, we are using the correct signs to **express** the **relation** between the rods of different lengths.

Express in the same way the relation between the lengths of the following **pairs** of rods:

the blue and the tan,
the black and the dark green,
the dark green and the yellow,
the pink and the light green.

4. $B=o-w$ tells us that the blue rod is **smaller than** the orange by the length of a white rod.

Express in the same way that the red is smaller than the light green,

the black than the tan,
the yellow than the dark green,

and **indicate** by writing the correct signs, that the difference is the length of a white rod.

5. Make a staircase starting with a white rod and use the red rod as the **common difference.**

When you have done it, fill in the gaps between the **successive** rods with red rods.

Make sure that the common difference is the size of a red rod.

Starting with the white and going up, what colors do you see?

Move down and say what you see.

Do it again with your eyes shut.

If we write $g=w+r$ to express the fact that the second rod in the staircase is the light green when the first is the white, and the common difference is equal to a red rod, what can we write about the other successive rods in this staircase?

Write it.

If we write $b=B-r$ to mean that the black rod is smaller than the blue by a red one, can you write down in the same way the difference between any two of the successive rods?

Write down the sequence of the colors of this staircase, both ways.

6. Now make a staircase starting with a red rod and with the red as common difference. Say which colors you see. Do it again with your eyes shut, first going up and then down.

If we write that $p=r+r$ to say that the pink is the second rod in this staircase, what shall we write to say that the dark green follows it, that the tan follows the dark green and the orange follows the tan?

If we write that $t=o-r$ to say that in this staircase the tan comes after the orange and that the difference is the red, what would you write to say that the dark green comes after the tan and the pink after the dark green?

Write down the sequence of the colors of this staircase, going up and then down.

7. Make a staircase starting with a white rod and with the common difference equal to the light green rod.

Read aloud what you see and fill in the gaps between successive rods, using light green rods. Is it right?

With your eyes shut, say which rods you have in your staircase, going up from the white and then coming down from the orange.

Write down the sequence of the colors in both directions.

If we write $o=b+g$ to say that the orange follows the black, what would you write to say that the pink is followed by the black?

If we write $w=p-g$ to say that the white is smaller than the pink by the light green, what would you write to say that the pink is smaller than the black and the black smaller than the orange, by the light green?

Equivalences

8. Using the correct words for the signs, read the following **equivalences**

$w+r=g$	$r+r=p$	$p+w=y$
$g-r=w$	$r-w=w$	$p-r=r$

and check with your rods to see whether these are true.

Read:

$w+w+r=p$	$r+w+r=y$	$w+w+g=y$

and form the trains they describe. Check and make sure they are right.

Form any pattern with your rods and write down equivalences you can see in it, using the signs above.

9. **Note** that $r+g=y$ can also be written as $g+r=y$, $y=g+r$ and $y=r+g$.
Check that these are true.
Write all the other **forms** for $r+w=g$ and $r+t=o$ and do the same for

$$p+w=y \qquad\qquad y+p=B$$
$$p=r+r \qquad\qquad d=p+r$$
$$p=g+w \qquad\qquad t=g+y$$
$$w+r+w=p \qquad\qquad w+d+r=B$$

Equations

10. We shall call an **equation** any of the **writings** that can be put down for a pattern that has two equivalent lengths. If one of the rods is missing from one of the lengths, we obtain further equations. Thus from $r+g=y$ we can obtain

$$r+\square=y \qquad\qquad \square+g=y \qquad\qquad r+g=\square$$

where the box $\square$ tells us that one rod has been removed.
What do the following tell us:

$$w+\square+w=p \qquad w+\square=g \qquad w+w+w+\square=y$$
$$r+\square=p \qquad y=\square+w \qquad p=w+w+w+\square$$

Form as many equations as you can and check them with your rods.
Can you say at once which rod or which signs are to be placed in the boxes?

$$w+r+w=g+\square \qquad\qquad w+\square+r=B$$
$$\square+w+w=r+r \qquad\qquad t+\square=o$$
$$r+p+\square=b+w \qquad\qquad b+r+\square=d+p$$
$$p+g+\square+r=b+g \qquad\qquad \square+w+r=B+r$$
$$w+r+g+p=\square+b \qquad\qquad d+r+w=t+\square$$

11. Write down the answers to

$p-w=\square$	$g-w=\square$	$d-p=\square$
$y-p=\square$	$b-y=\square$	$b-p=\square$
$d-y=\square$	$b-d=\square$	$d-w=\square$
$B-t=\square$	$t-p=\square$	$t-b=\square$
$B-b=\square$	$t-d=\square$	$t-r=\square$
$o-w=\square$	$o-p=\square$	$o-g=\square$
$o-B=\square$	$o-d=\square$	$o-b=\square$

12. Find what has been removed in

$b-\square=p$	$o-r=\square$	$\square-w=t$
$\square=B-b$	$\square-w=b$	$t-\square=p$
$d-\square=w$	$d-r=\square$	$\square-p=r$

Form your own equations like those above and find what should be placed in the box in each of them.

Brackets

13. If we take a yellow rod and place against it at one end, **first** a white rod, and **then** a red, what is left uncovered can be written

$y-w-r$

to indicate what we have done.
But if we first form the train $w+r$ and then place it against the yellow rod, we shall write

$y-(w+r)$

also to indicate what we have done.
Use your rods to make the following arrangements, and form them by one of these two methods, according to whether the writing includes ( ) or not.

$$y-r-r \qquad p-w-r \qquad y-g-w$$
$$B-d-w \qquad o-p-y \qquad t-w-p$$
$$y-(r+r) \qquad p-(w+r) \qquad y-(g+w)$$
$$B-(d+w) \qquad o-(p+y) \qquad t-(w+p)$$

14. Read:

$y-(r+r)=w$	Is it true?
$y-(g+w)=w$	Is it true?
$y-w-w=g$	Is it true?
$p-w-r=w$	Is it true?
$d-p-w=w$	Is it true?
$b-w-y=w$	Is it true?
$b-(w+g)=g$	Is it true?

Find the missing rod in

$$y-(r+\square)=r \qquad\qquad y-r-\square=w$$
$$y-(w+\square)=g \qquad\qquad \square-(w+r)=r$$
$$d-(w+\square)=w \qquad\qquad b-(\square+g)=w$$
$$B-(w+\square)=p \qquad\qquad o-(\square+d)=w$$

The name for ( ) is **brackets** or **parentheses**.

Figures and multiples

15. When we have $w+w$ or $g+g$ or $B+B$ we shall also write $2w$ or $2g$ or $2B$ and read **two** white rods or **two** of the light green rods or **twice** the blue rod. Read the following using these three ways of talking:

$$2o, \qquad 2d, \qquad 2p, \qquad 2b, \qquad 2r, \qquad 2t, \qquad 2y$$

Do not forget that they are equivalent forms for $o+o$, $d+d$ etc., and that you can always replace one by the other if you wish or need it.

Are the following true:

$$r+ r=2r=p \qquad 2w+r=g$$
$$2r+w=y \qquad 2r+2w=d$$
$$2r+2g=0 \qquad B-w=2p$$
$$b+w=2p \qquad d+p=2(g+r)$$

Which rod will be needed for

$$2r-\square=g \qquad 2\square+w=y$$
$$2(r+g)=B+\square \qquad 2(w+r)+\square=b$$

Make as many equations as you can using the **figure** 2 as we did above.

16. If we take **three** rods of one color and make a train with them we can write the following equivalent forms:

$$r+r+r=3r=2r+r=r+2r$$
$$g+g+g=3g=2g+g=g+2g$$

Write as above the forms for the trains using three rods.

If we take **four** rods of one color and make a train with them we can write the following equivalent forms:

$$d+ d+ d+ d=4d=2d+2d=3d+ d= d+3d$$
$$B+B+B+B=4B=2B+2B=3B+B=B+3B$$

Write as above the forms for the trains using four rods of one color.

If we take **five** rods of one color and make a train with them we can write the following equivalent forms:

$$t+t+t+t+t=5t=4t+t=3t+2t=2t+3t=t+4t$$

$b+b+b+b+b=5b=4b+b=3b+2b=2b+3b=$
$b+4b$

Write as above the forms for the trains using five rods of one color.

17.   Are the following true:

$2y=0$	$3g=B$	$4r=t$	$5r=0$
$2g=d$	$2p=t$	$3r+2w=t$	$4w+2r=t$

What are the following differences equivalent to?

$5r-2r=$ $\qquad$ $4r-p=$

$5r-3w=$ $\qquad$ $5r-2p=$

$3g-2r=$ $\qquad$ $2d-2r=$

$3p-2w=$ $\qquad$ $5g-y=$

$2b-t=$ $\qquad$ $2b-3g=$

$5r-(2w+2r)=$ $\qquad$ $3g-(3w+2r)=$

$4p-(2r+2g+w)=$ $\qquad$ $4y-(B+2w)=$

$4y-4p=$ $\qquad$ $2B-2b=$

$2(0+t)-2(B+b)=$ $\qquad$ $2(y+p)-(2w+2g)=$

18.   If we make trains taking **six** rods we write one of the forms $6g$ if the rods are green, or $6B$ if the rods are blue; read:

$6w$ $\quad$ $6d$ $\quad$ $6t$ $\quad$ $6y$ $\quad$ $6o$ $\quad$ $6r$ $\quad$ $6p$ $\quad$ $6b$

If we take **seven** rods we write $7b$ if the rods are black; read:

$7B$ $\quad$ $7w$ $\quad$ $7t$ $\quad$ $7o$ $\quad$ $7r$ $\quad$ $7d$ $\quad$ $7g$ $\quad$ $7y$ $\quad$ $7p$

If we take **eight** rods we write $8p$ if the rods are pink; read:

$8w$ $\quad$ $8o$ $\quad$ $8b$ $\quad$ $8B$ $\quad$ $8t$ $\quad$ $8y$ $\quad$ $8r$ $\quad$ $8d$ $\quad$ $8g$

If we take **nine** rods we write 9 o if the rods are orange; read:

9 b 9 p 9 w 9 t 9 d 9 g 9 y 9 B 9 r

If we take **ten** rods we write 10 w if the rods are white; read:

10 r 10 o 10 g 10 B 10 p 10 b 10 y 10 d 10 t

Write equivalent forms for

$$6\ t=$$
$$7\ p=$$
$$8\ b=$$
$$9\ o=$$
$$10w=$$

Find the differences equivalent to

$10w-5w=$	$10\ b-6\ b=$
$8B-4B=$	$7\ p-3\ p=$
$9\ d-2\ d=$	$6\ r-2\ r=$
$5\ o-2\ o=$	$6B-5B=$
$2w+3\ r-2g=$	$3\ p+2\ g-2d=$
$4\ b-4\ r-4g=$	$5\ d-(2d+3p)=$
$4\ d+2\ b-(3r+3p)=$	$5\ d+4\ b-5(w+r)=$

19.   Are the following true

$$o=10w=5\ r=2y$$
$$B=9w=3g$$
$$t=4\ r=2p=8w$$
$$b=7w$$
$$d=6w=3\ r=2\ g$$
$$y=5w$$

28

$$p = 4w = 2r$$
$$g = 3w$$
$$r = 2w$$

Names of fractions

20. Every time we see that one rod is equivalent to a train of other rods made of one color we can read as we have just done in No. 19.

Thus $B = 3g$ tells us that the blue rod is equivalent to a train made of three light green rods. We also say that B is **three times** as big or as long as the light green rod. Read in this way all the writings of No. 19.

But just as B is seen to be bigger than g, g is at the same time seen to be smaller than B, and we shall say that

B is three times as big as g and

g is **one third** as big as B or is **one third of** B and write $g = \frac{1}{3} \times B$ which we shall read as g is (equivalent to) one third of B

Read $g = 3w$ and $w = \frac{1}{3} \times g$

$d = 3\,r$ and $r = \frac{1}{3} \times d$

The following names are used when you read the first of these writings the other way round:

$r = 2w$	$w = \frac{1}{2} \times r$	*one half of*
$p = 2\,r$	$r = \frac{1}{2} \times p$	,, ,,
$d = 2\,g$	$g = \frac{1}{2} \times d$	,, ,,
$t = 2\,p$	$p = \frac{1}{2} \times t$	,, ,,
$o = 2\,y$	$y = \frac{1}{2} \times o$	,, ,,
$p = 4w$	$w = \frac{1}{4} \times p$	*one quarter of*
$t = 4\,r$	$r = \frac{1}{4} \times t$	*or one fourth of*

$y=5w$	$w=\frac{1}{5}\times y$	*one fifth of*
$o=5r$	$r=\frac{1}{5}\times o$	,, ,,
$d=6w$	$w=\frac{1}{6}\times d$	*one sixth of*
$b=7w$	$w=\frac{1}{7}\times b$	*one seventh of*
$t=8w$	$w=\frac{1}{8}\times t$	*one eighth of*
$B=9w$	$w=\frac{1}{9}\times B$	*one ninth of*
$o=10w$	$w=\frac{1}{10}\times o$	*one tenth of*

$\frac{1}{2}, \frac{1}{3}, \frac{1}{4}, \frac{1}{5}, \frac{1}{6}, \frac{1}{7}, \frac{1}{8}, \frac{1}{9}$, and $\frac{1}{10}$ are signs for **fractions.** You now know the names for fractions from **halves** to **tenths.**

21. Now that you know how to write so many of the **relationships** between the rods you will be able to work out the following in your head. If you cannot, use your rods.
Are the following true:

$3w+\frac{1}{3}\times B=d$ $\qquad$ $\frac{1}{7}\times b+\frac{1}{5}\times o=g$

$3(w+r)=\frac{1}{3}\times B+d$ $\qquad$ $4(r+w)=o+r$

$\frac{1}{2}\times t+\frac{1}{4}\times t=d$ $\qquad$ $\frac{1}{3}\times B+\frac{1}{3}\times g+\frac{1}{2}\times r=y$

$\frac{1}{2}\times t-\frac{1}{3}\times B=\frac{1}{2}\times r$ $\qquad$ $\frac{1}{3}\times B-\frac{1}{3}\times d=\frac{1}{2}\times r$

$o-(\frac{1}{2}\times t+\frac{1}{5}\times y)=\frac{1}{2}\times o$ $\quad$ $\frac{1}{5}\times o+\frac{1}{2}\times o=\frac{1}{2}\times t+\frac{1}{3}\times B$

Invent as many of these equivalences as you can think of. Write them down, check them with the rods, and show them to your teacher.

IV

NUMBER WORK
MEASURE
STUDY OF NUMBERS UP TO 10

Part IV

NUMBER WORK. MEASURE
STUDY OF NUMBERS UP TO 10

1. Let us measure all the rods using the white rod as the **unit.**

How many white rods will be needed to make a length equivalent to that of the red rod?

how many for the light green rod?

how many for the pink rod?

Find how many white rods will be needed to make equivalent lengths for all the different length rods, and write your answers using the following signs for the names you have just found:

for the white rod we need one white rod or 1

for the red rod we need two white rods or 2

for the light green rod we need three white rods or 3

for the pink rod we need four white rods or 4

yellow is equivalent to five white rods or 5

dark green is equivalent to six white rods or 6

black is equivalent to seven white rods or 7

tan is equivalent to eight white rods or 8

blue is equivalent to nine white rods or 9

orange is equivalent to ten white rods or 10.

When we write in this new way, we are using figures to show the length of each rod when measured by the white rod.

Addition and subtraction

2. Now we shall take the red rod and form its pattern.

What do we find?

How many white ones are needed to form a length equivalent to that of the red one?

If we take one of them away, what is left against the red rod?

For 'end to end' we shall use again the sign +.

What is 1+1 if you use the names of the colors of the rods?

What is 2−1 equivalent to?

3. Take the light green rod and form its pattern.

What do you find?

Write it down, using the sign +.

The white line is...

The white and red line is...

Can you put these two rods end to end another way?

How will you write it?

Let us write 3−1 for the pattern made by a green rod with a white rod placed on top, covering part of it at one end.

Which rod will cover the part that is left?

Name it by using a figure.

3−1=2 can also be read 'three minus one equals two'.

Read: 3−2=1

2−1=1

4. If we take a green rod and put a red one on top of it at either the right or the left end and

33

covering part of it, how much is left uncovered?
Say it using the names of the figures.
Write it down.

Read: $3-2=1$

$1=3-2$

Complete these patterns in writing:

$1+1=$	$2-1=$	$2=1+$
$-2=1$	$3-\ =1$	$1+1+1=$
$3=1+$	$-1=2$	$2+\ =3$
$1+1+\ =3$	$3-\ =2$	$1+\ =2$
$2+1=$	$3=2+$	$3=\ +2$

The pink rod

5. Make the pattern of the pink rod.
What do you find?
Write it all down using figures.
Have you got a line that can be read as $2+2$

or $3+1$

or $1+2+1$

or $1+1+1+1$?

How many red rods are there in the red line?
How many white ones are there in the white line?
How many rods in the red and white line?

Complete this written pattern:

$$1+1+2= \qquad 3+\ =4$$
$$1+3= \qquad 1+2+\ =4$$

34

6. With your rods find how much of the pink rod is left uncovered when we ask the following questions in writing

$$4-1=$$ $$4-3=$$
$$4-2=$$ $$4-(1+2)=$$

7. Complete these patterns in writing:

$$1+1+ =4$$ $$1+2=$$ $$3+ =4$$
$$4-2=$$ $$3+1=$$ $$2+1+ =4$$
$$3+ =4$$ $$2+ =4$$ $$4= +3$$
$$+1+2=4$$ $$1+1+ =3$$ $$4-3=$$
$$3-2=$$ $$4-1=$$ $$-2=2$$
$$1+ +1=4$$ $$-1=3$$ $$2+ +1=4$$
$$4=2+ +1$$ $$4=1+$$ $$+2+ =4$$

If you cannot do it, use the rods.

The yellow rod

8. Now take the yellow rod and form its pattern.
What do you find?
Write it down.

Read: $2+2+1=5$ $3+2=5$
$1+4=5$ $5=4+1$

Find what must be written in to complete the following

$$1+ +1=5$$ $$1+1+ +1=5$$
$$4+ =5$$ $$5= +3$$
$$5-2=$$ $$5=2+1+$$
$$2+ =5$$ $$1+2+ =5$$

9. **Say,** using the words one, two, three, four, five, plus, minus, is equivalent to or equals, what you see in the following patterns:

$5-4=1$	$3+2=5$	$2+2=4$
$1+3+1=5$	$2+1=3$	$3-2=1$
$4+1=5$	$4-1=3$	$4-2=2$
$5-2=3$	$4=5-1$	$3=5-2$

10. **Complete** the pattern by writing in what is missing:

$1+1+\ =4$	$3+\ =5$	$5=1+$
$3+\ +1=5$	$5-4=$	$4=5-$
$2+1+\ =5$	$3+\ =4$	$1+2+\ =5$
$5-(2+1)=$	$4-(1+2)=$	$3+1+\ =5$
$4=1+\ +1$	$4+\ =5$	$5-(3+1)=$
$2+\ =5$	$5-3=$	$5-(2+2)=$
$3-1=$	$2+2=$	$3-2=$

If you cannot do it use the rods.

Multiplication and fractions

11. Now let us write 2×2 for two red rods, and read it as **'two times two'**, 2×1 for two white ones, and read it as 'two times one', 3×1 for three white ones, and read it as 'three times one'.

Read:

2×3	4×1	$2\times2+1$
5×1	1×5	2×4
3×5	5×2	$2\times3-1$
$3+2\times1$	$2+1\times3$	$1\times3+2\times1$

12. Make 2×2 and $2+2$ with the rods.
What do you see?
Make $2 \times 2 + 1$ and $1+2+2$.
What do you see?
Make $3 \times 1 + 2$ and $2+1+1+1$ and $1+2+1+1$.
What do you see?

13. Write, using the signs $+$ and $\times$ the trains formed by

five white rods end to end
three white followed by a red
one red followed by two white.

14. Write the following expressions in a different way using the signs $\times$ or $+$:

$$1+1+1+2=5 \qquad 2 \times 1 + 3 = 5$$
$$1+2+1=4 \qquad 3+2 \times 1 = 5$$
$$2 \times 2 + 1 = 5 \qquad 1 \times 2 + 2 = 4$$
$$3 \times 1 = 3 \qquad 4 \times 1 = 4$$

15. Using the rods, find which of the following form the biggest lengths:

$$3 \times 1 \text{ or } 1+3 \text{ or } 3+1$$
$$2 \times 2 \text{ or } 3+1 \text{ or } 2+2$$
$$2+3 \text{ or } 2 \times 3 \text{ or } 3 \times 2$$
$$4+1 \text{ or } 4 \times 1 \text{ or } 1+4$$
$$5 \times 1 \text{ or } 1+5 \text{ or } 5+1$$

16. Can you say without using the rods which of the following is the smallest:

$$2+1 \text{ or } 2 \times 1$$
$$3 \times 1 \text{ or } 1+3$$

37

$$5 \times 1 \text{ or } 1+5$$
$$5 \times 1 \text{ or } 4 \times 1$$
$$4 \times 1 \text{ or } 3 \times 2$$
$$4 + 1 \text{ or } 2+3$$
$$1 + 5 \text{ or } 5 \times 1$$
$$2 \times 2 + 1 \text{ or } 2+2+1$$
$$2 \times 1 + 1 \text{ or } 3 \times 1$$

If you cannot, use the rods.

17. Write the answer to

$$1 + 2 \times 2 = \qquad 2 \times 2 + 1 =$$
$$3 \times 1 + 2 = \qquad 2 \times 1 + 2 =$$
$$2 \times 1 + 1 = \qquad 3 \times 1 + 1 =$$
$$1 \times 3 + 1 \times 2 = \qquad 1 \times 1 + 1 \times 4 =$$

18. And to

$$(4-2) \times 2 = \qquad 4 = 2 \times$$
$$3 + 2 \times 1 = \qquad 5 - 2 \times 1 =$$
$$(5-1) \times 1 = \qquad 1 \times 1 + = 4$$
$$3 \times 1 + = 4 \qquad 5 - 3 \times 1 =$$
$$5 - 1 \times 1 = \qquad 4 - (2 \times 1) =$$
$$5 - 2 \times 2 = \qquad 5 - (2 \times) = 1$$

19. Since $2 \times 2 = 2 + 2 = 4$, we can say that two red rods equal one pink rod.
Another way of saying this is that one red rod is **half** a pink rod.
We know that $2 \times 1 = 1 + 1 = 2$, or that two white rods equal one red rod.

38

We shall also say that one white rod is half a red
rod.

How many red rods make a pink rod?

How many white rods make a red rod?

How many times is the red rod needed to make
the pink rod?

How many times is the white rod needed to make
the red rod?

Which rod is half the red rod?

Which rod is half the pink rod?

20.   Give the answer in words: what is half
two? what is half four?

Write the answer: what is half 2? what is half 4?

    2 is what of 4?   1 is what of 2?

21.   When we write $2=\frac{1}{2}\times4$, we read it as
'two is half of four'.

Read: $1=\frac{1}{2}\times2$

and $\frac{1}{2}\times2+3$

       $3+\frac{1}{2}\times4$

       $\frac{1}{2}\times4+\frac{1}{2}\times2$

       $1+\frac{1}{2}\times4+3$

       $\frac{1}{2}\times2+1+\frac{1}{2}\times4+1$

22.   Complete these equations:

$\frac{1}{2}\times2=$ $\frac{1}{2}\times4=$ $2=\frac{1}{2}\times$

$\frac{1}{2}\times4+1=$ $3+\frac{1}{2}\times2=$ $\frac{1}{2}\times2+\frac{1}{2}\times4=$

$3-(\frac{1}{2}\times2)=$ $4+(\frac{1}{2}\times2)=$ $5-(\frac{1}{2}\times2)=$

$2+\frac{1}{2}\times2+\frac{1}{2}\times4=$ $5-(\frac{1}{2}\times\quad)=4$

23. If a white rod is half a red rod, show the other half.

If a red rod is half a pink rod, show the other half.

Show two halves of the red rod.

Put them end to end.

Is there a rod equal to the halves of the red rod end to end?

Show two halves of the pink rod.

Put them end to end.

Is there a rod equal to the two halves of the pink rod?

24. Show three halves of the red rod.

Put them end to end.

Is there a rod equal to the three halves of the red rod end to end?

Show three halves of the pink rod.

Put them end to end.

Is there a rod equal to the three halves of the pink rod?

25. We have written $\frac{1}{2} \times 2$ for one half of the red rod, and $\frac{1}{2} \times 4$ for half of the pink rod, so that

$$1 = \frac{1}{2} \times 2 \text{ and } 2 = \frac{1}{2} \times 4$$

We want to write that a light green rod is three halves of a red rod; as $\frac{1}{2}$ is read one half, $\frac{3}{2}$ is read three halves.

And we may write $3 = \frac{3}{2} \times 2$.

Since $\frac{1}{2} \times 2$ is 1 and $\frac{3}{2} \times 2$ is 3 and 4 is 3+1, we write 4 is $\frac{4}{2} \times 2$ and read it as '4 is four halves of 2'.

What would you write for five halves of 2?
and for two halves?

26. Complete these equations:

$\frac{1}{2}\times 2+1=$ $\frac{3}{2}\times 2+1=$

$\frac{3}{2}\times 2=$ $\frac{1}{2}\times 2+\frac{4}{2}\times 2=$

$\frac{3}{2}\times 2+2=$ $\frac{1}{2}\times 4+3=$

$\frac{1}{2}\times 4+2+\frac{1}{2}\times 2=$ $\frac{3}{2}\times 2-1=$

$\frac{1}{2}\times 4+\frac{3}{2}\times 2=$ $\frac{2}{2}\times 4=$

$\frac{1}{2}\times 4-\frac{1}{2}\times 2=$ $\frac{3}{2}\times 2+\frac{2}{2}\times 2=$

$\frac{2}{2}\times 2=$

27. How many white rods cover the light
green one?
Each of them is called **one third** of the light
green rod.
Show one third of the light green rod.
     and another third.
     and another third.
     and one more.
How many thirds of the light green rod have you
got?
Take two thirds of the light green rod.
Put them end to end.
Is there a rod equal to these two rods end to
end?
Find it.
Take four thirds of the light green rod.
Put them end to end.
Is there a rod equal to these four thirds of the
light green rod end to end?
Take five thirds of the light green rod.
Put them end to end.

Is there a rod equal to the five thirds of the light green rod?

28. We shall write $\frac{1}{3}$ for one third.
One third of the green rod is the white one, so we have $1 = \frac{1}{3} \times 3$.
But also $2 = 1 + 1 = \frac{1}{3} \times 3 + \frac{1}{3} \times 3 = \frac{2}{3} \times 3$
$$4 = 1 + 1 + 1 + 1 = \frac{4}{3} \times 3 = 2 + 2 =$$
$$\frac{2}{3} \times 3 + \frac{2}{3} \times 3$$
Also $\quad 3 = \frac{3}{3} \times 3$ and $5 = \frac{5}{3} \times 3$.

Complete these equations:

$\frac{2}{3} \times 3 =$	$\frac{1}{3} \times 3 =$
$\frac{2}{3} \times 3 + \frac{1}{3} \times 3 =$	$\frac{4}{3} \times 3 =$
$\frac{4}{3} \times 3 - \frac{1}{3} \times 3 =$	$\frac{1}{3} \times 3 + \frac{4}{3} \times 3 =$
$\frac{5}{3} \times 3 - 2 =$	$\frac{5}{3} \times 3 - \frac{2}{3} \times 3 =$
$\frac{5}{3} \times 3 - \frac{1}{2} \times 2 =$	$\frac{4}{3} \times 3 + 1 =$
$1 + \frac{1}{2} \times 2 + \frac{1}{3} \times 3 =$	$\frac{4}{3} \times 3 - \frac{1}{2} \times 2 =$
$5 - (\frac{1}{2} \times 2) =$	$4 - (\frac{1}{3} \times 3) =$
$3 - (\frac{1}{2} \times 4) =$	$2 - (\frac{1}{3} \times 3) =$

29. Which is bigger:
$$\frac{1}{2} \times 2 \text{ or } \frac{1}{3} \times 3?$$
$$\frac{2}{2} \times 2 \text{ or } \frac{2}{3} \times 3?$$
$$\frac{3}{2} \times 2 \text{ or } \frac{3}{3} \times 3?$$
$$\frac{3}{2} \times 2 \text{ or } \frac{2}{2} \times 4?$$
$$\frac{4}{2} \times 2 \text{ or } \frac{2}{2} \times 4?$$

30. How many white rods are needed to cover a pink rod?

Each is called one **quarter** or one **fourth** of the pink rod.

Find one quarter of the pink rod.

And another quarter, and another, and another, and another.

How many quarters of the pink rod have you got?

Take two of them and put them end to end.

Is there a rod equal to the two quarters of the pink rod end to end?

Take three of them and put them end to end.

Is there a rod equal to the three quarters of the pink rod end to end?

Take four of them and put them end to end.

Is there a rod equal to the four quarters of the pink rod end to end?

Is there one equal to five quarters?

31. We shall write $\frac{1}{4}$ for one quarter.

One quarter of the pink rod is the white one, so we have

$$1 = \frac{1}{4} \times 4$$

We shall also write
$$2 = 1 + 1 = \frac{2}{4} \times 4$$
$$3 = 1 + 1 + 1 = \frac{3}{4} \times 4$$
$$4 = 1 + 1 + 1 + 1 = \frac{4}{4} \times 4$$
$$5 = 1 + 1 + 1 + 1 + 1 = \frac{5}{4} \times 4$$

32. Since $4 = 2 + 2$ we can write it
$$\frac{2}{4} \times 4 + \frac{2}{4} \times 4 = \frac{4}{4} \times 4$$
Since $4 = 3 + 1$ we can write it $\frac{3}{4} \times 4 + \frac{1}{4} \times 4 = \frac{4}{4} \times 4$

Read the following expressions:
$$\frac{1}{4} \times 4 + \frac{1}{3} \times 3 + \frac{1}{2} \times 2 + 1 = 4$$
$$\frac{2}{4} \times 4 + \frac{2}{3} \times 3 + 1 = 5.$$

Are they right?

Complete the following equations:

$\frac{1}{2} \times 2 =$ $\frac{1}{3} \times 3 =$ $\frac{1}{4} \times 4 =$

$\frac{2}{2} \times 2 =$ $\frac{2}{3} \times 3 =$ $\frac{2}{4} \times 4 =$

$\frac{3}{2} \times 2 =$ $\frac{3}{3} \times 3 =$ $\frac{3}{4} \times 4 =$

$\frac{4}{2} \times 2 =$ $\frac{4}{3} \times 3 =$ $\frac{4}{4} \times 4 =$

$\frac{5}{2} \times 2 =$ $\frac{5}{3} \times 3 =$ $\frac{5}{4} \times 4 =$

And the following:

$\frac{5}{2} \times 2 - \frac{3}{2} \times 2 =$ $\frac{5}{2} \times 2 - \frac{4}{4} \times 4 =$

$\frac{3}{2} \times 2 + \frac{2}{3} \times 3 =$ $\frac{5}{4} \times 4 - \frac{3}{2} \times 2 =$

$\frac{4}{2} \times 2 + \frac{1}{4} \times 4 =$ $\frac{4}{3} \times 3 - \frac{1}{3} \times 3 =$

$\frac{5}{3} \times 3 - \frac{3}{4} \times 4 =$ $\frac{5}{2} \times 2 - \frac{4}{3} \times 3 =$

33. Which is bigger:

$\frac{5}{3} \times 3$ or $\frac{5}{2} \times 2$?

$\frac{4}{3} \times 3$ or $\frac{3}{2} \times 2$?

$\frac{1}{3} \times 3$ or $\frac{1}{4} \times 4$?

$\frac{1}{2} \times 4$ or $\frac{2}{2} \times 2$?

$\frac{3}{2} \times 2$ or $\frac{5}{3} \times 3$?

34. Complete the following equations:

$1 + \frac{1}{2} \times 2 + \frac{1}{3} \times 3 + \frac{1}{4} \times 4 =$

$2 + \frac{2}{2} \times 2 + \frac{1}{3} \times 3 =$

$1 + \frac{3}{2} \times 2 - \frac{1}{4} \times 4 =$

$\frac{4}{3} \times 3 - \frac{3}{2} \times 2 =$

$\frac{4}{4} \times 4 - \frac{3}{3} \times 3 =$

$4 + 1 - \frac{3}{2} \times 2 =$

$5 - \frac{4}{3} \times 3 + 2 =$

44

35. How many white rods are needed to cover a yellow one?

Each of them is called **one fifth** of the yellow rod and we write $\frac{1}{5}$ for one fifth.

Take one fifth of the yellow rod, then another one, another one, another one, and one more.

How many have you got?

Take two of them and put them end to end.

Is there a rod equal to two fifths of the yellow rod?

Take three of them and put them end to end.

Is there a rod equal to three fifths of the yellow rod?

Is there a rod equal to four fifths?

Is there one equal to five fifths?

36. Show one fifth of the yellow rod.

Show a rod that is two fifths of the yellow rod. Show one that is three fifths and one that is four fifths.

Which one is five fifths?

Now show one that is half the red rod.

One that is three halves of the red rod.

One that is one third of the light green rod.

One that is four thirds of the light green rod.

What is the red rod of the light green rod?

Take two red rods and put them end to end.

If the red rod is two thirds of the light green rod, what will the two red rods end to end be?

What is the yellow rod of the light green?

What is the light green of the yellow?

What is the pink of the light green, and the light green of the pink?

What is the pink of the yellow?

45

37. The red is two thirds of the light green; what is the pink of the light green?
The red is two fifths of the yellow; what is the pink of the yellow?
Write down what the white is of the red
                                        of the light green
                                        of the pink
                                        of the yellow
     and what the red is of the white
                                        of the red
                                        of the light green
                                        of the pink
                                        of the yellow
   and what the light green is of the white
                                        of the red
                                        of the light green
                                        of the pink
                                        of the yellow
    and what the pink is of the white
                                        of the red
                                        of the light green
                                        of the pink
                                        of the yellow
  and what the yellow is of the white
                                        of the red
                                        of the light green
                                        of the pink
                                        of the yellow

38. Using only the five smallest rods, say which pairs of rods will give the following:
$\frac{1}{3}, \frac{1}{2}, \frac{1}{4}, \frac{2}{3}, \frac{3}{3}, \frac{3}{4}, \frac{4}{4}, \frac{2}{2}, \frac{2}{4}, \frac{1}{5}, \frac{5}{4}, \frac{3}{5}, \frac{3}{1}, \frac{2}{5}, \frac{4}{5}.$

39. Complete the following equations:

$5-3=$

$\frac{5}{3}\times 3-\frac{1}{4}\times 4+2=$

$\frac{1}{5}\times 5+\frac{1}{4}\times 4+\frac{1}{3}\times 3-\frac{1}{2}\times 2-1=$

$\frac{1}{5}\times(3+2)=$

$\frac{1}{2}\times(3+1)-\frac{1}{4}(5-1)=$

$1+2+2=$

$\frac{1}{2}\times 4+\frac{1}{4}\times 4=$

$\frac{1}{2}\times 4+\frac{2}{3}\times 3=$

$\frac{1}{3}\times(5-2)=$

$\frac{1}{2}\times 4+\frac{3}{8}\times 3=$

$\frac{1}{4}\times(5-1)=$

Division

40. How many red rods can we put end to and to make a yellow rod?

Which rod is needed to complete the length?

Can we write it: $5=2\times 2+1$?

We can read this as **'two twos and one make five'**.

How many twos **go into** 5?

If we take 1 from 5, how many times two have we left?

41. When we ask 'how many 2's in 5?' or 'how many 3's in 4?' we say that we are asking a **division** question; such questions can be written in two ways:

$$5\div 2 \text{ or } 2\overline{)5}$$
$$4\div 3 \text{ or } 3\overline{)4}$$

The two writings on the left can also be read as

divide 5 by 2 or divide 4 by 3

and the answers are 2 and **remainder** 1 for the first

1 and remainder 1 for the second

47

Which can be written

$5 \div 2 = 2$ r. 1

$4 \div 3 = 1$ r. 1 where r is read remainder.

The second form of these writings can be read as: **How many twos in five** or How many threes in four and the answers then take the form:

2 and 1 over

1 and 1 over

which can be written

$$\begin{array}{r} 2 \\ 2\overline{)5} \\ 1 \end{array}$$ 2 and 1 over

$$\begin{array}{r} 1 \\ 3\overline{)4} \\ 1 \end{array}$$ 1 and 1 over

Write the answers to the following questions in the way shown above:

$5 \div 4$	$5 \div 3$	$5 \div 1$
$4 \div 2$	$4 \div 1$	$4 \div 4$

When nothing is left we do not write anything as for example in

$$3 \div 3 \text{ we write } 3\overline{)3}^{\,1}$$

The four operations at once

42. What is half $(5-1)$? one third of $(5-2)$? or of $(4-1)$? two thirds of $(5-2)$? two thirds of $(4-1)$? one quarter of $(3+1)$? two quarters of $(5-1)$? three fifths of $(3+2)$? four fifths of

48

$(1+4)$? two halves of 2 and three quarters of 4 end to end?

43. Complete:

$\frac{1}{2}\times(3+1)+\frac{1}{4}\times(5-1)+\frac{1}{3}\times(5-2)=$

$\frac{2}{3}\times(5-2)+\frac{2}{4}\times(3+1)-\frac{1}{2}\times(5-1)=$

$1+2-\frac{1}{2}\times(3+1)+\frac{1}{4}(5-1)=$

$\frac{2}{3}\times(4-1)-\frac{1}{3}\times(5-2)+\frac{2}{5}\times(3+2)=$

Equivalent expressions

44. We already know that $1 = 2 - 1$ or $3 - 2$ or $4 - 3$ or $5 - 4$, that $1 = \frac{1}{2}\times 2$ or $\frac{1}{3}\times 3$ or $\frac{1}{4}\times 4$ or $\frac{1}{5}\times 5$. If we replace 2 by $1+1$ or 3 by $2+1$ or $1+2$ or $1+1+1$ or any other writing that we know is equivalent to it, we shall say that we write **equivalent expressions.** They look very different but the answer is the same.

Thus $\frac{1}{2}\times 2+\frac{1}{3}\times 3$ is equivalent to $1+1$ and to 2.
$\quad\frac{1}{4}\times 4+\frac{1}{5}\times 5+\frac{2}{3}\times 3$ is equivalent to $1+1+2$ and to 4.

But also $1+1$ can be written as $\frac{1}{2}\times 2+\frac{1}{4}\times 4$ or $\frac{1}{5}\times 5+2-1$ or $\frac{1}{3}\times(5-2)+\frac{1}{4}\times(5-1)$.

Write as many **different** equivalent expressions as you can think of and check your answers.

The study of 6

45. Now take the dark green rod.
Make its pattern and write it down using the figures above and calling the dark green rod 6. Take away the rods that are at the right end of each row of the pattern and put them with the rest.

49

Can you put them back without any mistakes, picking up the right rod every time?
If you can, take them away again. If you cannot, look again at your pattern before taking them away.
Now, without putting them back, write down which you think they should be.
When you have done it, show it to your teacher.
Begin again with another pattern of 6, and this time take away the rod at the left end of each row.

46. Complete, in writing, the following patterns:

3+2+1=	2+4=	1+5=
3+1+ =6	4+ =6	6=1+
+3+2=6	6= +2	5=6−
6−(1+2)=	5−2+3=	4+1−2+3=
2×2+ =6	3+2×1=	4×1+ =6
6−5=	6=2+2×	6−2=2×

47. If we cover the dark green rod with light green ones, how many do we need?
What can we say each of them is, compared with the dark green rod?
If we cover the dark green rod with red ones, how many do we need?
What can we say each of them is of the dark green rod?
What is $\frac{1}{2} \times 6$? And $\frac{1}{3} \times 6$?
Find a rod that is $\frac{2}{3} \times 6$. What is its value?
Cover the dark green rod with white ones. Each of them is called one sixth of the dark green, and

we write it $\frac{1}{6}$ for **one sixth.**

What is $\frac{1}{6} \times 6$? and $\frac{2}{6} \times 6$? and $\frac{3}{6} \times 6$? and $\frac{4}{6} \times 6$? and $\frac{5}{6} \times 6$? and $\frac{6}{6} \times 6$?

48. Compare $\frac{2}{3} \times 6$ and $\frac{4}{6} \times 6$. Which is bigger? which is smaller?

Compare $\frac{1}{2} \times 6$ and $\frac{3}{6} \times 6$.

Now compare $\frac{2}{3} \times 6$ and $\frac{5}{6} \times 6$. How much must we add to the smaller one to get the bigger one?

How much must we take away from the bigger one to get the smaller one?

We can write this in a number of ways:

$$\frac{2}{3} \times 6 \text{ is } 4, \ \frac{5}{6} \times 6 \text{ is } 5$$

$$4 + 1 = 5 \text{ or } \frac{2}{3} \times 6 + 1 = 5 \text{ or } \frac{2}{3} \times 6 + 1 = \frac{5}{6} \times 6$$

$$\text{or } \frac{4}{6} \times 6 + \frac{1}{6} \times 6 = \frac{5}{6} \times 6$$

$$\text{or } \frac{2}{3} \times 6 + \frac{1}{6} \times 6 = \frac{5}{6} \times 6$$

$$\text{and } 5 - 1 = 4 \text{ or } \frac{5}{6} \times 6 - 1 = 4 \text{ or } \frac{5}{6} \times 6 - \frac{1}{6} \times 6 = 4$$

$$\text{or } \frac{5}{6} \times 6 - \frac{1}{6} \times 6 = \frac{4}{6} \times 6$$

$$\text{or } \frac{5}{6} \times 6 - \frac{1}{6} \times 6 = \frac{2}{3} \times 6.$$

All these different writings are new examples of equivalent expressions.

49. Give as many different equivalent expressions as you can for the following:

$2 + 3 = 5$	$5 - 3 = 2$	$5 - 2 = 3$
$1 + 2 = 3$	$3 - 1 = 2$	$3 - 2 = 1$
$4 + 2 = 6$	$6 - 3 = 3$	$6 - 1 = 5$
$3 + 1 + 2 = 6$	$2 + 3 - 4 + 5 = 6$	$4 + 2 - 1 = 5$

Products, crosses and factors

50. Since $2 \times 3 = 6$ and $3 \times 2 = 6$, two light green rods side by side can be covered by three

red ones side by side. Try it. These two **rectangles** of rods can be replaced by a cross, red over green, which we shall read as 'two times three'. When we make a green over red cross, we shall read it as 'three times two'. These two **products** 2×3 and 3×2 are equivalent to 6.

We shall call 2 and 3 **factors** of 6.

But as 1×6 and 6×1 also give 6, 1 and 6 are also factors of 6.

Cardboard material

51. Find in the wallchart the sign that is red and light green.

And let us place the counter marked 6 on the white circle, and call the red 2 and the light green 3.

Let us take the pink rod and form it with red rods.

How many do we need?

We know that $2 \times 2 = 4$. Which cross will be the one that stands for 4?

What are the colors in it?

Can you find the sign in the wallchart that represents 4?

Place the counter marked 4 on the white circle and call the red part of the sign 2. We shall read this sign as 2 times 2, and we know it is 4.

52. Look at the pack of cards. Which is the one that represents 6? And 4?

Take a few of the cards. Can you find the one we may call 6? And the one we may call 4?

53. How many threes in 6? and how many twos?

How many twos in 4?

How many twos in 2? and how many fours in 4?

How many ones in 5? and in 6? And in 3?

How many twos in 3? and in 5?

How many threes in 5? and in 4?

How many fours in 6? and in 5?

Write the answers to

$$2\overline{)6} \qquad\qquad 3\overline{)5} \qquad\qquad 3\overline{)6}$$

$$4\overline{)6} \qquad\qquad 2\overline{)4} \qquad\qquad 5\overline{)6}$$

Study of 7

54. Take a black rod and make its pattern. Complete the following equations:

$5+2=$ $6+1=$ $2+5=$

$4+\ =7$ $-3=4$ $7-2=$

$2+3+\ =7$ $2\times3+\ =7$ $3+4=$

$1+2+3+\ =7$ $7-(2+3)=$ $7-\frac{5}{6}\times6=$

$\frac{1}{2}\times4+\frac{1}{2}\times6=7-$ $7=3+(\frac{1}{3}\times\ )+2$ $7-1=$

$3\times\ +1=7$ $7-\frac{1}{2}\times6=$ $3\times2+\ =7$

$\frac{2}{3}\times6+\frac{3}{5}\times5=$ $7-(\frac{1}{3}\times\ )=5$

$\frac{1}{2}\times2+\frac{1}{3}\times3+\frac{1}{4}\times4+\frac{1}{5}\times5+\frac{1}{6}\times6=7-(\frac{1}{2}\times\ )$

If you cannot do it use the rods.

55. How many white rods cover the black one?

We shall call each of them **one seventh** of the
black rod and write it $\frac{1}{7}$ or $\frac{1}{7}\times 7$.
Show $\frac{2}{7}\times 7$. Find a rod equal to $\frac{2}{7}$ of the black
one.
Show $\frac{3}{7}$, $\frac{4}{7}$, $\frac{5}{7}$, $\frac{6}{7}$ of the black rod.
Each time find one rod that is the same length as
these.
Check these examples of equivalent expressions.

$$7=4+3=\tfrac{4}{7}\times 7+\tfrac{3}{7}\times 7$$
$$=4-2+\tfrac{5}{7}\times 7$$
$$=\tfrac{4}{7}\times 7-\tfrac{4}{6}\times 6+7$$
$$=\tfrac{2}{3}\times 6+2+1$$
$$=\tfrac{2}{3}\times 3+\tfrac{3}{4}\times 4+\tfrac{1}{2}\times 4$$
$$=\tfrac{1}{3}\times(7-4)+2\times 3$$
$$=\tfrac{4}{5}\times(4+1)-\tfrac{1}{2}\times 4+5$$

Invent and write down some examples of your
own, and show them to your neighbour to check.

Study of 8

56. Take a tan rod and make its pattern. Complete in writing:

$4\times 2=$

$3+\ =8$

$8=2\times 2+$

$8-(2+1)=$

$\tfrac{1}{3}\times 6+2=8-$

$\tfrac{1}{5}\times(8-3)=8-$

$\tfrac{1}{2}\times 4+\ =8$

$8-7=$

$1+2+3+\ =8$

$6+\ =8$

$+1=8$

$8-\tfrac{1}{2}\times 4=$

$7-2+\ =8$

$\tfrac{1}{2}\times(8-2)=$

$3+\tfrac{4}{5}\times 5=8-$

$\tfrac{1}{4}\times 4+\ +2=8$

$8-3=$

$5+\ =8$

54

$$8 - \tfrac{3}{5} \times 5 =$$
$$7 + 1 - 3 =$$
$$\tfrac{1}{3} \times (4 + 2) + 2 =$$
$$1 + 3 + \tfrac{1}{2} \times 6 + \tfrac{1}{4} \times 4 =$$
$$\tfrac{2}{5} \times 5 + \tfrac{3}{4} \times 4 = 8 -$$

$$8 - \tfrac{1}{4} \times 4 =$$
$$7 + \tfrac{1}{2} \times 2 =$$

If you cannot do it, use the rods.

57. How many white rods cover the tan one?

We shall call each of them **one eighth** of the tan rod and write it $\tfrac{1}{8}$ of 8 or $\tfrac{1}{8} \times 8$.

Show $\tfrac{2}{8}, \tfrac{3}{8}, \tfrac{4}{8}, \tfrac{5}{8}, \tfrac{6}{8}, \tfrac{7}{8}, \tfrac{8}{8}$ of the tan rod.

Each time find one rod that is the same length as these.

Do for the tan rod what you did in No. 47 for the dark green rod and record your findings.

Are the following equations true?

$$\tfrac{1}{4} \times 8 = 2$$
$$\tfrac{1}{4} \times 8 + \tfrac{1}{2} \times 8 + \tfrac{1}{8} \times 8 = 7$$
$$\tfrac{1}{8} \times 8 = \tfrac{1}{6} \times 6 = \tfrac{1}{4} \times 4$$

$$\tfrac{3}{4} \times 8 = 6$$
$$\tfrac{2}{4} \times 8 = 4$$

Check that these are equivalent expressions

$$8 = 2 \times 4 = 2 + 2 + 4$$
$$= \tfrac{1}{2} \times 8 + 4$$
$$= 2 \times 3 + \tfrac{2}{7} \times 7$$
$$= \tfrac{3}{8} \times 8 + \tfrac{1}{2} \times 6 + 2$$
$$= \tfrac{3}{6} \times 6 + 2 + \tfrac{3}{8} \times 8$$
$$= \tfrac{1}{2} \times (4 + 4) + \tfrac{6}{7} \times 7 - 2$$
$$= \tfrac{2}{3} \times 3 + \tfrac{2}{5} \times 5 + \tfrac{4}{6} \times 6$$

Invent and write some examples of your own, and give them to your neighbour to check.
Find the sign for 8 on the wallchart and also its card in the pack.

Study of 9

58. Take a blue rod and make its pattern. Complete in writing:

$5+4=$

$9-3=$

$1+2+3+\ =9$

$9-(2+3)=$

$9=8+$

$\frac{1}{5}\times(8-3)=\ -8$

$\frac{1}{6}\times(9-3)=$

$4\times2+\ =9$

$9=\ +7$

$3\times2+\ =9$

$9-2\times3=$

$9-\frac{1}{2}\times4=$

$\frac{4}{5}\times(9-4)=$

$2+2\times3+\ =9$

$2\times4+1=$

$6+\ =9$

$3\times3=$

$9-2\times2=$

$9=8-7+$

$\frac{1}{2}\times6+\frac{3}{5}\times5+\frac{3}{4}\times4=$

$\frac{1}{2}\times(9-7)+\frac{1}{4}\times(9-5)=$

$\frac{1}{3}\times9=$

$\frac{2}{3}\times9=$

$\frac{1}{3}\times9+\frac{1}{2}\times8=$

$\frac{1}{3}\times9-\frac{1}{4}\times8+\frac{1}{3}\times6=$

If you cannot do it, use the rods.

59. How many white rods cover the blue one? We shall call each of them one ninth of the blue rod and write it $\frac{1}{9}$ of 9 or $\frac{1}{9}\times9$.
Show $\frac{2}{9}, \frac{3}{9}, \frac{4}{9}, \frac{5}{9}, \frac{6}{9}, \frac{7}{9}, \frac{8}{9}$ of the blue rod.
Each time find one rod that is the same length as these.

56

Make examples of your own, and show them to your neighbour to check.

Are these expressions equivalent?

$$9 = 3 \times 3 = 2 \times 4 + 1$$
$$= 3 \times (\tfrac{3}{9} \times 9)$$
$$= \tfrac{3}{9} \times 9 + \tfrac{3}{9} \times 9 + 3$$
$$= \tfrac{1}{2} \times 2 + 8$$
$$= 4 + \tfrac{1}{4} \times 4 + 3 + \tfrac{1}{8} \times 8$$
$$= 3 \times 2 + 1 + 1 + 1$$
$$= \tfrac{3}{7} \times 7 + \tfrac{4}{8} \times 8 + \tfrac{1}{2} \times 4$$
$$= \tfrac{3}{4} \times (9 - 5) + \tfrac{6}{7} \times 7$$

Find more equivalent expressions.

Find the sign for 9 on the wallchart and also its card in the pack.

Study of 10

60.   Take an orange rod and make its pattern. Complete in writing:

$1 + \quad = 10$

$2 \times 5 =$

$2 \times 2 + 2 \times 3 =$

$\tfrac{1}{2} \times 4 + \tfrac{1}{3} \times 6 = 10 -$

$9 + \tfrac{1}{2} \times (5 - \quad) = 10$

$\tfrac{1}{7} \times (10 - \quad) = 1$

$10 - 5 =$

$10 - \quad = 2 \times 4$

$10 - \tfrac{1}{2} \times (8 - 2) =$

$2 \times 4 + \quad = 10$

$\tfrac{1}{2} \times (10 - 4) + \tfrac{1}{3} \times (10 - 7) = 10 -$

$3 + 7 =$

$9 + \quad = 5 + 4 + 1$

$3 \times 3 + \quad = 10$

$3 + \tfrac{4}{5} \times 5 = 10 -$

$\tfrac{2}{3} \times (10 - \quad) = 6$

$6 + \tfrac{3}{4} \times \quad = 10 - 1$

$8 + \tfrac{1}{4} \times (10 - 6) =$

$\tfrac{1}{6} \times (10 - 4) =$

If you cannot do it, use the rods.

57

61.   How many white rods cover the orange one?

We shall call each of them **one tenth** of the orange rod and write it $\frac{1}{10}$ of 10 or $\frac{1}{10} \times 10$.

Show $\frac{2}{10}, \frac{3}{10}, \frac{4}{10}, \frac{5}{10}, \frac{6}{10}, \frac{7}{10}, \frac{8}{10}, \frac{9}{10}, \frac{10}{10}$ of the orange rod.

Each time find one rod that is the same length as these.

Make up examples of your own, and give them to your neighbour to check.

Are these expressions equivalent?

$$10 = 5 \times 2 = 3 + 3 + 4$$
$$= \tfrac{4}{6} \times (10 - 4) + 2 \times 3$$
$$= \tfrac{1}{2} \times 10 + \tfrac{5}{6} \times 6$$
$$= 1 + 3 + \tfrac{6}{10} \times 10$$
$$= \tfrac{1}{2} \times 2 + \tfrac{3}{4} \times 4 + \tfrac{5}{6} \times 6 + 1$$
$$= \tfrac{2}{7} \times (9 - 2) + \tfrac{8}{10} \times 10$$
$$= \tfrac{3}{10} \times 10 + \tfrac{7}{10} \times 10$$
$$= 2 \times 3 + \tfrac{1}{4} \times 4 + \tfrac{4}{5} \times (7 - 2) - 1$$

62.   How many red rods cover the orange rod?
How many yellow rods cover the orange rod?

Is $4 = \tfrac{2}{5} \times 10$?

What is 6 of 10? and 8 of 10?

Are the following true?

$$\tfrac{2}{5} \times 10 + \tfrac{1}{3} \times 9 = \tfrac{1}{2} \times 6 + \tfrac{2}{5} \times 5 + \tfrac{1}{4} \times 4$$
$$\tfrac{1}{2} \times 8 + \tfrac{1}{2} \times 10 = \tfrac{1}{2} \times 6 + \tfrac{1}{2} \times 8 + 2$$
$$\tfrac{3}{5} \times 10 + 4 = \tfrac{6}{5} \times 5 + 2 \times 2$$

58

Add your own inventions.
Find the sign for 10 on the wallchart and also its card in the pack.

Exercises

63. Compare $\frac{2}{4} \times 8$ and $\frac{1}{2} \times 8$; which is bigger?
Compare $\frac{3}{4} \times 8$ and $\frac{2}{2} \times 8$ and $\frac{4}{4} \times 8$; which is bigger?
Compare $\frac{3}{9} \times 9$ and $\frac{1}{3} \times 9$; which is bigger?
Compare $\frac{2}{3} \times 9$ and $\frac{6}{8} \times 6$; which is bigger?

64. Complete the equations:

$\frac{1}{7} \times (8-1) =$ $\frac{4}{9} \times (4+5) =$

$\frac{1}{8} \times (9-1) =$ $\frac{3}{10} \times (7+3) =$

$\frac{1}{9} \times (10-1) =$ $\frac{1}{10} \times (2 \times 2 + 2 \times 3) =$

$\frac{1}{10} \times (2 \times 5) =$ $2 \times 4 + \frac{1}{5} \times 10 =$

$\frac{2}{7} \times (9-2) =$ $\frac{3}{4} \times (6+2) - \frac{1}{5} \times 10 =$

$\frac{1}{8} \times (10-2) =$ $10 - \frac{1}{2} \times (7+3) = 9 -$

$\frac{2}{9} \times (7+2) =$ $\frac{1}{2} \times 10 + \frac{1}{5} \times 10 =$

$\frac{1}{10} \times (9+1) =$ $\frac{3}{10} \times (3 \times 3 + 1) =$

$\frac{2}{7} \times (10-3) =$ $\frac{1}{7} \times (9-2) + \frac{4}{5} \times (8+2) =$

$\frac{2}{8} \times (5+3) =$ $9 - 1 + 2 - 3 =$

$\frac{1}{7} \times (9-2) + \frac{1}{8} \times (9-1) + \frac{3}{9} \times (9+1) =$ $1 + 2 + 3 + 4 =$

Test

65. Give the answers to the following questions as quickly as you can:

Half of ten? a third of nine? three quarters of eight?

59

If you take away two from half of ten, how much is left?

If you add a third of nine to a quarter of eight, what is the answer?

Add four to five, take away seven, add six and halve it. How much have you got?

Half ten and half eight is how many times three?

By how much is three quarters of eight and two fifths of ten bigger than nine?

Add one tenth and three fifths of ten.

More exercises with the staircases

66. Take your rods, choose one of each color, and form a staircase.

Read it aloud, using the number names for the rods, moving first up from the white rod and then moving down from the orange rod.

Write down the two sequences of numbers.

67. What is the difference between any two successive rods?

$10 = 9 + 1$ tells us that the orange rod is bigger than the blue rod by the length of the white one.

What do $8 = 7 + 1$

$5 = 4 + 1$

$3 = 2 + 1$

$2 = 1 + 1$ tell us?

Express in the same way the relation between
the blue and the tan,
the black and the dark green,
the dark green and the yellow,
the pink and the light green.

68. $9 = 10 - 1$ tells us that the blue is smaller than the orange by the length of the white rod. Express in the same way the fact that

the red is smaller than the light green,
the black is smaller than the tan,
the yellow smaller than the dark green, and that the difference is equivalent to a white rod.

69. Make a staircase starting with a white rod and with the red rod as the common difference.

When you have done it, fill in the gaps between successive rods with a red rod.

Starting with the white and going up, what are the numbers for the rods in this staircase. Read them going up and then coming down.

Now do it with your eyes shut.

If we write $3 = 1 + 2$ to express the fact that the second rod is the light green when the first is the white and the difference the length of the red rod, what can we write about any other two successive rods in this staircase?

Write it down.

If we write $7 = 9 - 2$ to express the fact that the black rod is smaller than the blue by the length of a red, what will you write to express the difference between all the successive rods?

Write down the sequence of numbers in this staircase, both ways.

70. Now make a staircase starting with a red rod and with the red as common difference.

Say which colors you see, and then name the

numbers they correspond to. Do it again with your eyes shut, first going up and then down.
If we write 4=2+2 to show that the pink is the second rod in this staircase, what shall we write to say that the dark green follows it, that the tan follows the dark green and the orange follows the tan?

71. If we write 8=10−2 to say that in this staircase the tan is placed after the orange and that the difference is the red rod, what would you write to say that the dark green comes after the tan and the pink after the dark green?
Write down the sequence of the numbers of this staircase, going up and down.

72. Using what you found in Part II No.37 about odd and even lengths, find from the staircase made up of one rod of each of the colors which represent the odd numbers and which the even numbers.
Is 3 an odd number or an even number?
Is 4 an odd number or an even number?
Is 7 an odd number or an even number?
Write down the odd numbers between 1 and 10.
Write down the even numbers between 1 and 10.

73. Which rods can be covered by an even number of white rods? and by an odd number of white rods?
Which rods can be covered by an odd number of red rods? and by an even number of red rods?

Can you find a rod that can be covered by an odd number of red rods and an even number of white ones?

Can you find one that can be covered by an even number of white rods and an even number of light green ones?

And one that can be covered by an odd number of white rods and by an odd number of light green ones?

Is it possible to make a length with an even number of red rods equal to a length made of an odd number of white rods?

When other rods are called 1

74. We have seen in Part III Nos. 19 and 20 that each rod has several equivalent names. For example, we know that

$$w=\tfrac{1}{2}\times r=\tfrac{1}{3}\times g=\tfrac{1}{4}\times p=\tfrac{1}{5}\times y \text{ etc.}$$

Each rod can serve as a unit. When any one of them has been chosen for that purpose the others will have new names.

Let us find the names of all the rods when the white is called one and written 1.

$$r= \qquad g= \qquad p= \qquad y= \qquad d=$$
$$b= \qquad t= \qquad B= \qquad o=$$

when the red is called one and written 1.

$$w= \qquad g= \qquad p= \qquad y= \qquad d=$$
$$b= \qquad t= \qquad B= \qquad o=$$

when the light green is called one and written 1.

$$w= \qquad r= \qquad p= \qquad y= \qquad d=$$
$$b= \qquad t= \qquad B= \qquad o=$$

when the pink is called one and written 1.

$$w= \quad r= \quad g= \quad y= \quad d=$$
$$b= \quad t= \quad B= \quad o=$$

when the yellow is called one and written 1.

$$w= \quad r= \quad g= \quad p= \quad d=$$
$$b= \quad t= \quad B= \quad o=$$

when the dark green is called one and written 1.

$$w= \quad r= \quad g= \quad p= \quad y=$$
$$b= \quad t= \quad B= \quad o=$$

when the black is called one and written 1.

$$w= \quad r= \quad g= \quad p= \quad y=$$
$$d= \quad t= \quad B= \quad o=$$

when the tan is called one and written 1.

$$w= \quad r= \quad g= \quad p= \quad y=$$
$$d= \quad b= \quad B= \quad o=$$

when the blue is called one and written 1.

$$w= \quad r= \quad g= \quad p= \quad y=$$
$$d= \quad b= \quad t= \quad o=$$

when the orange is called one and written 1.

$$w= \quad r= \quad g= \quad p= \quad y=$$
$$d= \quad b= \quad t= \quad B=$$

V

APPLICATIONS

Part V

APPLICATIONS

1. If you have ten rods how many can you give to each of

ten boys?
five boys?
two boys?

If there were three boys, how many would each get? and if there were four?

2. How many rods would you need in order to give one each to nine boys? Two each to four? Three each to three? Five each to two?

3. You want to give ten colored cards to a friend; you buy two at first, then three and then two more. How many do you still need to find?

4. Two boys and one girl pick flowers in a garden.
The boys have three each and the girl four.
How many flowers have they got altogether?

5. Mother has eight candies to share between her two boys. She gives half of them to each. How many will each receive?

66

6. When I give away half the rods I have, I still have five left. How many did I have at first?

7. Three children each want to take one third of a number of candies, and each gets three. How many were there to start with?

8. Every school day a child takes one apple to school and eats one at home. He goes to school five days a week. How many apples does he get in all?

9. How many bags containing three apples each would you need if you had nine apples? And if you had eight? Or ten?

10. You have a collection of seven cards, and every day you give away one. For how long can you do that?

11. You want to make ten drawings for the school wall and you have only made three. How many more have you still got to do?

12. You are playing a game with matchsticks. You start with seven and you first win two, then lose three and again two, and win one and lose three again and win four. How many have you got at the end?

13. I lost half what I had and I still have four. Then I lost half of these and half of the rest. How many did I start with? And how many have I got left?

14. Our hens laid two, then one, then three, then four eggs this week. How many did they lay?

15. I went up our staircase two by two, and after five steps I reached the landing. How many stairs are there?

16. If there are ten stairs in a staircase and you can go up three at a time, how many steps must you take to reach the landing?

17. A quarter of my rods are red and the rest are orange. I give away one orange and there are five left. How many rods did I have?

18. There were four of us at dinner and we ate eight bananas. My father said we ate four-fifths of what we had. How many did we have?

19. If with four sevenths of my money I can buy four cookies, how many can I buy with five sevenths or three sevenths of it? And what part of my money is left in each case?

20. After giving away four of my ten candies, I share the rest between three of us. How many do we each get?

21. With two thirds of our allowance we buy half a pound of chocolate. How much more could we buy with the rest of our money?

22. I can write words of 5, 7, 4, 9, 3, 8 letters. Which is the longest of these words? And which is the shortest?

23. Find the numbers which lie between 1 and 3; 3 and 5; 5 and 7; 7 and 9. Add the two you started with and compare the result with twice the one in the middle. What do you notice?

24. Add 1+2+3 and divide by three.
Add 2+3+4 and divide by three.
Add 3+4+5 and divide by three.
What do you notice?

25. Make stories like the ones you had earlier, using the following arrangements of the rods and the writings that go with them:

(i) a yellow and a red rod equal a black rod:

$5+2=7$

(ii) two pink rods equal a tan rod:

$4+4=8$ $\qquad$ $2\times4=8$ $\qquad$ $4=\frac{1}{2}\times8$

(iii) to make a length equal to that of a black rod, starting with the light green, we need a pink rod:

$7-3=4$

(iv) the yellow is made of five white rods, and nine white ones make a blue:

$5=5\times1$ $\quad$ $9=9\times1$ $\quad$ $5=\frac{5}{9}\times9$ $\quad$ $9=\frac{9}{5}\times5$

(v) three light green rods make a blue, a blue and white make an orange:

69

$$3 \times 3 = 9 \qquad 9 + 1 = 10 \qquad 3 \times 3 + 1 = 10$$
$$3 = \tfrac{1}{3} \times (10 - 1) \qquad\qquad 10 = 3 \times 3 + \tfrac{1}{3} \times 3$$
$$\tfrac{10}{3} = 3 + \tfrac{1}{3}$$

(vi) two pink and one red make an orange:

$$2 \times 4 + 2 = 10 \qquad\qquad 4 = \tfrac{1}{2} \times (10 - 2)$$
$$2 \times 4 + \tfrac{1}{2} \times 4 = 10 \qquad\qquad \tfrac{10}{4} = 2 + \tfrac{1}{2}$$

VI

STUDY OF NUMBERS UP TO 20

Part VI

STUDY OF NUMBERS UP TO 20

1. Make staircases with the rods, first starting with a white, then a red, then a light green rod and so on, with a common difference between the strips equal to a pink, a yellow, a dark green rod and so on.

Write down what you see and give the sequences of numbers that form the staircases, going up from the smallest rod and coming down from the biggest.

2. We shall now put any two rods end to end and compare their length with that of the orange rod.

Can you find which pairs are smaller than the orange rod?

When you find a pair which is bigger than the orange rod, find which rod you must put end to end with the orange to make the two lengths equal.

Try with a yellow and a dark green. Which rod do you need?

Try with a yellow and a black.

a yellow and a tan.

a yellow and a blue.

a yellow and an orange.

3. Do this again, starting with a dark green and trying with all the rods that give a length bigger than the orange. Find each time which rod you must put end to end with the orange to make the two lengths equal.

4. Repeat this with a black, a tan and a blue rod.

5. When it is the white rod that we must put end to end with the orange, we say the length is **eleven** and we write it 11.
When it is the red rod, we call the length **twelve** and we write it 12.
When it is the light green, we say it is **thirteen,** and we write 13.
Find what you must add to nine to get eleven, twelve and thirteen.

$9+ \ =11$　　　　$9+ \ =12$　　　　$9+ \ =13$

Find what must be added to 8 to make 12, 11, and 13.

$8+ \ =12$　　　　$+8=11$　　　　$13=8+$

Find what must be added to seven, to six, to five, to four, to three.

Complete the equations:

$10+ \ =13$	$12=7+$	$10=12-$
$11-9=$	$8+ \ =11$	$13=6+$
$2+ \ =11$	$3+ \ =12$	$5+6=$
$7+4=$	$4+ \ =11$	$11= \ +7$
$6+ \ =13$	$12=8+$	$5+ \ =12$
$2\times6=$	$3+9=$	$8+ \ =12$
$13-5=$	$13-4=$	$13-7=$

73

Study of 11

6. Make a pattern for 11 and write down what you see.

Complete the following equations:

$2+9=$ $5+6=$

$2\times 5+1=$ $3\times 3+2=$

$1+2+3+4=11-$ $11-(5+4)=$

$11-\frac{1}{2}\times 6=$ $\frac{1}{2}\times 6+\frac{1}{2}\times 8=11-$

$\frac{1}{2}\times (11-9)=$ $\frac{1}{3}\times (11-2)=$

$11-9+3=$ $11-8+5=$

$$3+8=$$
$$11-3\times 3=$$
$$11-(2\times\ )=3$$
$$\tfrac{1}{3}\times 9+\ =11$$
$$\tfrac{2}{7}\times (11-4)=$$
$$11-6+4-3+2=$$

If you cannot do it, use the rods.

Check that the following are equivalent expressions for 11.

$$11=6+3+2=6+\tfrac{5}{8}\times (6+2)$$
$$=2\times 3+\tfrac{5}{7}\times (3+4)$$
$$=\tfrac{1}{3}\times 6+2\times (7-3)+1$$
$$=10+\tfrac{1}{2}\times 2$$
$$=1+8+\tfrac{2}{3}\times (4+5)-4$$
$$=3+\tfrac{1}{2}\times 4+\tfrac{6}{7}\times 7$$
$$=\tfrac{2}{5}\times (3+2)+3\times 3$$
$$=11-4+\tfrac{2}{3}\times 3+\tfrac{1}{2}\times 4.$$

74

7. How many twos in eleven? how much is left?

How many threes in eleven? how much is left?
How many fours in eleven? how much is left?
How many fives in eleven? how much is left?
Since eleven white rods cover the length eleven, each white one is called **one eleventh** of eleven, and we write $\frac{1}{11}$ of 11 or $\frac{1}{11} \times 11$.

Find a rod which is $\frac{2}{11} \times 11$, one that is $\frac{5}{11} \times 11$, one that is $\frac{7}{11} \times 11$ and one that is $\frac{10}{11} \times 11$.

Study of 12

8. Make a pattern for 12 and write down what you see.

Complete the following patterns in writing:

$9+ \ =12$

$+5=12$

$12-(1+2+3)=$

$2\times 5+1=12-$

$\frac{3}{2}\times 6=12-$

$12-11+10=$

$10+ \ =12$

$2\times 6=$

$12-2\times 5=$

$3\times 3+ \ =12$

$3+(2\times \ )+1=12$

$12-9-1+3=$

$1+ \ =12$

$6+2\times 3=$

$12-(2\times \ )=4$

$12-2=2\times$

$\frac{2}{5}\times(12-2)=$

$12-10+5-6=$

If you cannot do it, use the rods.

9. Try to make the length of twelve using rods of one color only for each line.

75

How many dark green rods do you need?
how many pink?
how many light green?
how many red?
Put two dark green rods side by side and six red rods side by side.
Can you cover the reds with the two dark green?
Can you cover the two dark green with the reds?
Try to do the same thing with the three pink rods and the four light green ones.
We can see that two dark green rods equal six red rods which equal three pink rods which equal four light green rods, and we can write:

$$12 = 2 \times 6 = 6 \times 2 = 3 \times 4 = 4 \times 3.$$

The four numbers 2, 3, 4, 6 are factors of 12. 2×6, 6×2, 3×4, 4×3 are products. These are all equal to 12.
We represent the first two, 2×6 and 6×2, by a cross made of a red and a dark green rod.
We represent the last two, 3×4 and 4×3, by a cross made of a light green and a pink rod.
12 is shown in the wall chart by a sign formed of these two pairs of colors. Can you find it?
Can you find it in the pack of cards?

10. How many sixes are there in twelve?
How many fives in twelve? how much is left?
How many fours in twelve?
How many threes in twelve?
How many twos in twelve?
What is half of twelve or $\frac{1}{2} \times 12$?
What is a third of twelve or $\frac{1}{3} \times 12$?
What is a quarter of twelve or $\frac{1}{4} \times 12$?

76

What is a sixth of twelve or $\frac{1}{6} \times 12$?

Since twelve white rods cover the length orange
+ red, the length of each white rod is called
one twelfth of it, and we write $\frac{1}{12}$ of 12 or $\frac{1}{12} \times 12$.

Compare $\frac{2}{12} \times 12$ and $\frac{1}{6} \times 12$.

Compare $\frac{3}{12} \times 12$ and $\frac{1}{4} \times 12$.

Compare $\frac{4}{12} \times 12$ and $\frac{1}{3} \times 12$.

Compare $\frac{6}{12} \times 12$ and $\frac{1}{2} \times 12$.

Which is bigger $\frac{5}{12} \times 12$ or $\frac{2}{3} \times 12$?

Which is smaller $\frac{4}{6} \times 12$ or $\frac{2}{3} \times 12$?

Find the value of

$\frac{9}{12} \times 12$ $\qquad$ $\frac{11}{12} \times 12$ $\qquad$ $\frac{5}{6} \times 12$ $\qquad$ $\frac{3}{4} \times 12$.

Study of 13

11. Make a pattern for 13 and write it down.
Complete these equations:

$13 - 4 =$ $\qquad$ $13 - 11 =$

$7 + \quad = 13$ $\qquad$ $13 = 2 \times 5 +$

$2 \times 3 + \quad = 13$ $\qquad$ $13 - \frac{1}{2} \times 12 =$

$13 - (1 + 2 + 3 + 4) =$ $\qquad$ $13 - \frac{1}{2} \times 10 + 3 =$

$13 - \frac{1}{2} \times 12 =$ $\qquad$ $\frac{2}{3} \times 12 + \frac{5}{12} \times 12 =$

$\frac{2}{7} \times (13 - 6) =$ $\qquad$ $\frac{4}{7} \times (13 - 6) + 9 =$

$\frac{3}{5} \times (13 - 3) + \quad = 11$ $\qquad$ $13 - 6 + 3 + 1 =$

If you cannot do it, use the rods.

Make examples of your own and show them to
your neighbour for him to check.

How many threes in thirteen? how much is left?

How many fours in thirteen? how much is left?

How many sixes in thirteen? how much is left?

Can you find a train of one color that makes the
length equivalent to thirteen, besides the one with
white rods.

12. Since thirteen white rods are needed, to make the length thirteen, each white one is called **one thirteenth** of thirteen, and we write $\frac{1}{13}$ of 13 or $\frac{1}{13} \times 13$.

Find a rod which is $\frac{4}{13} \times 13$, and one that is $\frac{6}{13} \times 13$, one that is $\frac{7}{13}$ of 13 and one $\frac{10}{13}$ of 13.

Check that the following are equivalent expressions:

$$13 = 3 \times 4 + 1 = 6 + 7$$
$$= 3 \times (\tfrac{1}{3} \times 12) + 1$$
$$= \tfrac{3}{7} \times 7 + \tfrac{8}{10} \times 10 + 2$$
$$= 10 - (\tfrac{1}{2} \times 12) + 9$$
$$= 12 - (11 - 9) + 3$$
$$= \tfrac{8}{12} \times 12 + \tfrac{3}{11} \times 11 + 2$$
$$= 4 + 3 + (3 \times 2)$$

Numbers 14, 15, 16 and 17

13. For the length orange and pink we say **fourteen** and write 14.

For the length orange and yellow we say **fifteen** and write 15.

For the length orange and dark green we say **sixteen** and write 16.

For the length orange and black we say **seventeen** and write 17.

$$14 = 10 + 4 \text{ and } 4 + 10$$
$$15 = 10 + 5 \text{ and } 5 + 10$$
$$16 = 10 + 6 \text{ and } 6 + 10$$
$$17 = 10 + 7 \text{ and } 7 + 10$$

Check the following with your rods:

$$14 = 5 + 6 + 3 = 7 + 4 + 3 = 9 + 1 + 4$$
$$14 = 2 \times 5 + 4 = 3 \times 4 + 2 = 9 + 5$$

78

$15 = 3 \times 5 = 9 + 6 = 8 + 7 = 11 + 4$
$16 = 9 + 7 = 2 \times 8 = 2 \times 7 + 2 = 3 \times 5 + 1$
$16 = 12 + 4 = 15 + 1 = 7 + 3 + 6 = 2 \times 5 + 2 \times 3$
$17 = 2 \times 8 + 1 = 5 \times 3 + 2 = 10 + 5 + 2 = 2 \times 7 + 3$

Make examples of your own and show them to your neighbour for him to check.

Study of 14

14. Make a pattern for 14 and write it down. Complete the following:

$5 + = 14$ $\qquad$ $9 + = 14$ $\qquad$ $8 + = 14$

$14 - 7 =$ $\qquad$ $14 - 11 =$ $\qquad$ $14 - (3 + 9) =$

$14 - (2 \times) = 2$ $\quad$ $11 + = 14$ $\qquad$ $2 \times 5 + 4 =$

$\frac{1}{2} \times 12 + \frac{1}{3} \times 9 = 14 - $ $\qquad$ $\frac{1}{7} \times (10 - 3) + \frac{8}{5} \times (14 - 9) =$

$\frac{2}{3} \times (14 - 5) + 7 =$ $\qquad$ $14 - 10 + 4 - 2 =$

$\frac{1}{2} \times (14 - 10) = 14 - $ $\qquad$ $14 - 7 + 5 - 2 =$

15. See whether you can make the length 14 using rods of only one color.
Which colors do you need to complete the length?
Put two black rods side by side and seven red ones side by side. Can you cover the black rods with red ones? and the red rods with the black ones?
We now know that $14 = 2 \times 7 = 7 \times 2$.
What are the factors of 14?
Can you find the sign for 14 in the wallchart?
What colors will you look for?
Can you find it in the pack of cards?

16. How many twos are there in fourteen?
How many sevens in fourteen?

79

How many fives in fourteen? and how much is left?

How many sixes in fourteen? and how much is left?

How many fours in fourteen? and how much is left?

How many threes in fourteen? and how much is left?

What is half of fourteen or $\frac{1}{2} \times 14$?

What is a seventh of fourteen or $\frac{1}{7} \times 14$?

Since fourteen white rods cover the length fourteen each white rod is called one fourteenth or $\frac{1}{14}$ of the length: $\frac{1}{14}$ of 14 or $\frac{1}{14} \times 14$.

Compare $\frac{2}{14} \times 14$ and $\frac{1}{7} \times 14$.

Compare $\frac{7}{14} \times 14$ and $\frac{1}{2} \times 14$.

What is $\frac{5}{7} \times 14$? and $\frac{10}{14} \times 14$?

Which is bigger $\frac{5}{7} \times 14$ or $\frac{1}{2} \times 14$?

Which is smaller $\frac{8}{7} \times 14$ or $\frac{11}{14} \times 14$?

17. Complete the following in writing:

$10 + \frac{1}{2} \times 4 + 2 =$ $\frac{1}{2} \times (14-6) + \frac{1}{7} \times 14 = 14 -$

$\frac{3}{7} \times 14 =$ $3 \times 4 - 4 \times 1 + \ = 14$

$1 + 2 + 3 + 4 = 14 -$ $\frac{5}{7} \times 14 =$

$2 \times 3 + \frac{1}{3} \times (14 - 11) =$

$2 \times (\frac{2}{3} \times 6) + \ = 14$

$\frac{2}{3} \times (14 - 2) + \frac{2}{7} \times (13 + 1) =$

$\frac{5}{6} \times (14 - 2) + \frac{2}{3} \times (14 - 8) =$

$\frac{2}{5} \times (14 - 4) + \frac{3}{5} \times (14 - 9) + \frac{4}{7} \times (14 - 7) =$

$\frac{1}{2} \times (\frac{1}{3} \times 12) + \frac{1}{3} \times (\frac{1}{2} \times 12) = 14 -$

$3 \times (\frac{1}{2} \times 6) + \frac{1}{3} \times 9 = 14 -$

$\frac{1}{2} \times 2 + \frac{1}{3} \times 3 + \frac{1}{4} \times 4 + \frac{1}{5} \times 5 + \frac{1}{6} \times 6 + \frac{1}{7} \times 7 = 14 -$

If you cannot do it, use the rods.

Study of 15

18. Make a pattern for 15 and write it down. Complete the following in writing:

$9+6=$ $\qquad$ $15=7+$ $\qquad$ $15-6=$

$10+3+\ =15$ $\qquad$ $12+\ =15$ $\qquad$ $15-4=$

$\frac{4}{7}\times(15-1)=7+$ $\qquad$ $2\times7+\ =15$ $\qquad$ $15-(2\times\ )=5$

$\frac{1}{2}\times(15-7)+\frac{1}{3}\times(15-6)=$ $\qquad$ $\frac{1}{2}\times10+\frac{1}{3}\times9=15-$

$\frac{2}{3}\times12+\frac{5}{7}\times(14-7)+2=$ $\qquad$ $2\times3-1+2\times5=$

$\frac{4}{7}\times(15-8)+\frac{3}{5}\times(15-10)=15-$

$4\times1+3\times2+\frac{1}{2}\times4+\frac{2}{6}\times6=$

19. Make 15 using rods of one color only. When you cannot do it with rods of one color only, complete the length with another. Which are the rods of one color that make 15? The numbers of these are called the factors of 15. Which are they?
What is 3×5? and 5×3?
Form a cross with them. Can you find the sign for these products in the wallchart? in the pack of cards?
Put the three yellow rods side by side and the five light green ones side by side. Can you cover one block of rods with the other?
Make one length by putting them end to end. What is that length?

20. How many twos are there in fifteen? and how much is left?
How many threes in fifteen? and how much is left?

How many fours in fifteen? and how much is left?

How many sixes in fifteen? and how much is left?

How many sevens in fifteen? and how much is left?

What is $\frac{1}{3} \times 15$? and $\frac{2}{3} \times 15$?

What is $\frac{1}{5} \times 15$? and $\frac{2}{5} \times 15$? and $\frac{3}{5} \times 15$? and $\frac{4}{5} \times 15$?

Compare $\frac{1}{3} \times 15$ and $\frac{2}{5} \times 15$; which is smaller?

Compare $\frac{2}{5} \times 15$ and $\frac{4}{5} \times 15$; which is bigger?

Since fifteen white rods cover the length fifteen, each white rod is one fifteenth or $\frac{1}{15}$ of 15, or $\frac{1}{15} \times 15$.

Compare $\frac{1}{3} \times 15$ and $\frac{5}{15} \times 15$.

Compare $\frac{2}{3} \times 15$ and $\frac{10}{15} \times 15$.

Compare $\frac{1}{5} \times 15$ and $\frac{3}{15} \times 15$.

Compare $\frac{2}{5} \times 15$ and $\frac{6}{15} \times 15$.

Compare $\frac{3}{5} \times 15$ and $\frac{9}{15} \times 15$.

Compare $\frac{4}{5} \times 15$ and $\frac{12}{15} \times 15$.

Compare $\frac{5}{5} \times 15$ and $\frac{15}{15} \times 15$.

21. Complete the following in writing:

$2 \times 5 + \quad = 15$ $\qquad$ $13 + \quad = 15$

$\frac{1}{3} \times 15 + \frac{2}{7} \times 14 = 15 -$ $\qquad$ $15 - 11 =$

$15 - (1 + 2 + 3 + 4) =$ $\qquad$ $15 - (9 + 3) =$

$\frac{4}{15} \times 15 + \frac{3}{13} \times 13 + \frac{8}{14} \times 14 =$ $\qquad$ $\frac{3}{2} \times (15 - 13) =$

$\frac{2}{5} \times 15 - \frac{3}{7} \times 14 = 12 -$ $\qquad$ $13 + (\frac{2}{5} \times \quad) = 15$

$\frac{2}{3} \times 15 + \frac{1}{5} \times 15 =$ $\qquad$ $2 \times (\frac{1}{3} \times 15) =$

$\frac{2}{7} \times (15 - 1) + \frac{3}{5} \times 10 = \frac{2}{3} \times$ $\qquad$ $\frac{2}{5} \times 15 - \frac{1}{3} \times 15 + 14 =$

$15 - 14 + 13 - 12 + 11 - 10 =$

If you cannot do it, use the rods.

Exercises

22. By how much is 15 bigger than 12?
By how much is 9 smaller than 14?
By how much must we increase 2×5 to get 13?

Which is bigger $\quad \frac{1}{8} \times 12$ or $\frac{1}{3} \times 15$?

$\qquad\qquad \frac{2}{3} \times 12$ or $\frac{2}{3} \times 15$?

Which is smaller $\quad \frac{1}{4} \times 12$ or $\frac{1}{5} \times 15$?

$\qquad\qquad \frac{1}{3} \times 12$ or $\frac{2}{5} \times 15$?

Compare $\frac{1}{5} \times 10$, $\frac{1}{7} \times 14$, $\frac{1}{6} \times 12$, $\frac{1}{4} \times 8$, $\frac{1}{3} \times 6$, $\frac{1}{2} \times 4$.

Compare $\frac{1}{5} \times 5 + \frac{1}{5} \times 10$ and $\frac{1}{5} \times 15$.

Compare $\frac{1}{3} \times 3 + \frac{1}{3} \times 9$ and $\frac{1}{3} \times 12$.

Compare $\frac{1}{2} \times 14 - \frac{1}{2} \times 6$ and $\frac{1}{2} \times 8$.

Compare $\frac{1}{4} \times 12 - \frac{1}{4} \times 8$ and $\frac{1}{4} \times 4$.

Study of 16

23. Make a pattern for 16 and write it down.
Complete the following in writing:

$10 + \quad = 16$ $\qquad 16 - 6 =$ $\qquad\quad 9 + \quad = 16$

$4 + 7 + \quad = 16$ $\qquad 2 \times 8 =$ $\qquad\quad 2 \times 7 + 2 =$

$3 \times 5 + \quad = 16$ $\qquad 2 \times 5 + 4 = 16 -$ $\quad 4 + (2 \times \quad) = 16$

$\frac{2}{7} \times (16 - 2) =$ $\qquad 16 - 11 =$ $\qquad\quad 16 - 3 \times 4 =$

$5 \times 2 + 5 = 16 -$ $\qquad\qquad \frac{3}{5} \times (16 - 6) =$

$4 \times 3 + \frac{1}{2} \times 8 =$ $\qquad\qquad \frac{4}{9} \times (16 - 7) =$

$1 + 2 + 3 + 4 + 5 = 16 - \qquad 16 - \frac{2}{7} \times (16 - 2) =$

$\frac{1}{2} \times 4 + \frac{1}{3} \times 6 + \frac{1}{4} \times 8 + \frac{1}{5} \times 10 + \frac{1}{6} \times 12 = 16 -$

$16 - 14 + 12 - 10 + 8 - 6 + 4 - 2 =$

If you cannot do it, use the rods.

24. Make 16 using rods of one color only. When you cannot do it with only one color, complete the length with rods of another.

Which of these rods make 16 exactly?

These numbers are called the factors of 16.

Which are they?

What is 2×8? and 8×2? and 4×4?

Form a cross with 8 and 2 and with 4 and 4. Can you find the sign for these products in the wall-chart? in the pack of cards?

Put the two tan rods side by side and the eight red ones side by side. Can you cover one block of rods with the other?

Are they the same length when put end to end?

What is the length?

Make a square with four pink rods. Put them end to end. What length do they make? Can you say that 4 is also a factor of 16?

25. How many twos are there in sixteen?

How many threes in sixteen? and how much is left?

How many fours in sixteen?

How many fives in sixteen? and how much is left?

How many sixes in sixteen? and how much is left?

How many sevens in sixteen? and how much is left?

What is half of sixteen or $\frac{1}{2} \times 16$?

What is a quarter of sixteen or $\frac{1}{4} \times 16$?

What is one eighth of sixteen or $\frac{1}{8} \times 16$?

Since sixteen white rods cover the length sixteen, each white one is one sixteenth of that length, or $\frac{1}{16}$ of 16, or $\frac{1}{16} \times 16$.

26. Compare $\frac{1}{4} \times 16$ and $\frac{4}{16} \times 16$.
Compare $\frac{2}{4} \times 16$ and $\frac{8}{16} \times 16$.
Compare $\frac{3}{4} \times 16$ and $\frac{12}{16} \times 16$.
Compare $\frac{1}{4} \times 16$, $\frac{2}{4} \times 16$ and $\frac{8}{16} \times 16$.
Compare $\frac{1}{8} \times 16$ and $\frac{2}{16} \times 16$.
Compare $\frac{2}{8} \times 16$, $\frac{4}{16} \times 16$ and $\frac{1}{4} \times 16$.
Compare $\frac{3}{8} \times 16$ and $\frac{6}{16} \times 16$.
Compare $\frac{4}{8} \times 16$, $\frac{8}{16} \times 16$, $\frac{2}{4} \times 16$ and $\frac{1}{2} \times 16$.
Compare $\frac{5}{8} \times 16$ and $\frac{10}{16} \times 16$.
Compare $\frac{6}{8} \times 16$, $\frac{12}{16} \times 16$ and $\frac{3}{4} \times 16$.
Compare $\frac{7}{8} \times 16$ and $\frac{14}{16} \times 16$.
Compare $\frac{16}{16} \times 16$, $\frac{8}{8} \times 16$, $\frac{4}{4} \times 16$ and $\frac{2}{2} \times 16$.

Complete the following:
$2 \times 7 + 1 = 16 -$ $3 \times (16 - 12) + 3 =$
$\frac{1}{2} \times (16 - 8) =$
$2 \times (\frac{1}{8} \times 16) =$
$\frac{3}{4} \times 16 - \frac{3}{8} \times 16 + \frac{3}{16} \times 16 =$
$\frac{3}{8} \times 16 + \frac{3}{10} \times 10 + \frac{2}{9} \times (16 - 7) =$
$10 + 4 - 3 + 5 - 4 + 2 =$
$2 \times 5 + 2 \times 2 - 3 \times 1 + 4 \times 1 = 16 -$
$\frac{1}{3} \times 15 + \frac{1}{5} \times 15 + \frac{1}{2} \times 16 =$
$\frac{1}{2} \times 10 + \frac{1}{5} \times 10 + \frac{1}{2} \times 14 + \frac{1}{4} \times 8 =$
$16 - 15 + 14 - 13 + 12 - 11 + 10 - 9 =$
If you cannot do it, use the rods.

85

Study of 17

27. Make a pattern for 17 and write it down. Complete the following in writing:

$8+ =17$ $17-13=$

$+10=17$ $17= +7$

$17= +9$ $17=11+$

$2\times5+ =17$ $17-2\times6=$

$17-\frac{1}{2}\times(10-4)=$ $\frac{1}{2}\times(17-7)=$

$\frac{3}{4}\times(17-3)=$ $17=15+(\frac{1}{2}\times)$

$13+\frac{1}{4}\times16=$ $1+2+3+4+5=17-$

$17-5=$ $17=7+$

$2\times8+ =17$ $17-3\times4=$

$\frac{1}{5}\times(17-12)=$ $14+\frac{1}{3}\times(15-6)=$

$14+(3\times)=17$

$\frac{1}{2}\times4+\frac{1}{4}\times8+\frac{1}{8}\times16+ =17$

$1\times1+3\times2+(2\times)=17$

$15-\frac{2}{3}\times(17-2)=17-$

$17-16+15-14+13-12+11-10=$

28. How many eights are there in seventeen? and how much is left?

How many sevens in seventeen? and how much is left?

How many sixes in seventeen? and how much is left?

How many fives in seventeen? and how much is left?

How many fours in seventeen? and how much is left?

How many threes in seventeen? and how much is left?

How many twos in seventeen? and how much is left?

Since seventeen white rods cover the length seventeen, each white rod is one seventeenth of that length, and we write $\frac{1}{17}$ of 17 or $\frac{1}{17} \times 17$.

Find a rod equal to $\frac{8}{17}$ of 17, and one equal to $\frac{6}{17}$.

Compare $\frac{9}{17} \times 17$ and $\frac{8}{15} \times 15$.

Compare $\frac{7}{17} \times 17$ and $\frac{7}{10} \times 10$.

By how much is 17 greater than 3×5?

By how much is 17 smaller than $12 + 7$?

Study of 18

29. An orange and a tan rod end to end make a length which we call **eighteen** and write 18.

Make a pattern for eighteen and write it down. Complete the following equations:

$9 + \ = 18$ $11 + \ = 18$ $2 \times 6 + \ = 18$

$18 - \ = 6$ $18 - \ = 11$ $18 - 2 \times 4 = 2 \times$

$2 \times 9 =$ $2 \times 8 + \ = 18$ $\frac{1}{3} \times (18 - 12) =$

$18 - 2 \times 7 =$ $18 - (\frac{1}{2} \times 10) =$ $18 - (\frac{3}{4} \times 16) =$

$10 + 3 + \ = 18$ $13 - 7 + \ = 18$ $\frac{2}{3} \times (18 - 6) =$

$18 - 16 + \frac{1}{8} \times 16 =$ $18 - 15 + 3 \times 5 =$

$18 - 10 + \frac{1}{2} \times 16 =$ $12 - 1 + 5 + \ = 18$

$\frac{1}{3} \times 12 + \frac{2}{7} \times 14 + \frac{5}{6} \times 12 =$ $2 \times 3 + (2 \times \ ) = 18$

If you cannot do it, use the rods.

30. How many nines are there in eighteen? and how much is left?

How many eights in eighteen? and how much is left?

How many sevens in eighteen? and how much is left?

How many sixes in eighteen? and how much is left?

How many fives in eighteen? and how much is left?

How many fours in eighteen? and how much is left?

How many threes in eighteen? and how much is left?

How many twos in eighteen? and how much is left?

What is a half of eighteen or $\frac{1}{2} \times 18$?

What is a third of eighteen or $\frac{1}{3} \times 18$?

What is a sixth of eighteen or $\frac{1}{6} \times 18$?

What is one ninth of eighteen or $\frac{1}{9} \times 18$?

What is $\frac{2}{9} \times 18$? and $\frac{2}{3} \times 18$? and $\frac{1}{6} \times 18$?

Compare $\frac{1}{9} \times 18$ and $\frac{1}{3} \times 18$.

Compare $\frac{2}{6} \times 18$, $\frac{1}{3} \times 18$ and $\frac{2}{9} \times 18$.

Since eighteen white rods cover the length eighteen, each white rod is one eighteenth of that length and we write it $\frac{1}{18}$ of 18 or $\frac{1}{18} \times 18$.

What is $\frac{2}{18} \times 18$? $\frac{3}{18} \times 18$? $\frac{5}{18} \times 18$? $\frac{7}{18} \times 18$? $\frac{11}{18} \times 18$?

Compare $\frac{2}{18} \times 18$ and $\frac{1}{9} \times 18$.

Compare $\frac{3}{18} \times 18$ and $\frac{1}{6} \times 18$.

Compare $\frac{4}{18} \times 18$ and $\frac{2}{9} \times 18$.

Compare $\frac{6}{18} \times 18$, $\frac{3}{9} \times 18$ and $\frac{1}{3} \times 18$.

Compare $\frac{8}{18} \times 18$ and $\frac{4}{9} \times 18$.

88

Compare $\frac{10}{18} \times 18$ and $\frac{5}{9} \times 18$.

Compare $\frac{12}{18} \times 18$, $\frac{6}{9} \times 18$ and $\frac{2}{3} \times 18$.

Compare $\frac{14}{18} \times 18$ and $\frac{7}{9} \times 18$.

Compare $\frac{16}{18} \times 18$ and $\frac{8}{9} \times 18$.

Compare $\frac{18}{18} \times 18$, $\frac{9}{9} \times 18$, $\frac{6}{6} \times 18$, and $\frac{3}{3} \times 18$.

31. What are the factors of 18?

Can you find in the wallchart the sign that shows the colors for these factors? and in the pack of cards?

By how much is 18 bigger than 13? and than 11?

By how much is 18 bigger than 3×5? and than 2×6? and than 7×2?

Which of the following is the biggest:

3×6	$7+9$	$3 \times 2 + 4 \times 3$
2×7	$11+6$	$10 + \frac{1}{2} \times 16$

Study of 19

32. An orange and a blue rod end to end make a length which we call **nineteen** and write 19.

Make a pattern for 19 and write it down.

Complete the following in writing:

$9+ =19$	$19=13+$	$19=17+$
$+3=19$	$12+ =19$	$19-11=$
$19-2 \times 5=$	$19-7 \times 2=$	$19-(2+7)=$
$19-3-6=$	$19-1-10+4=$	
$1+2 \times 2+3 \times 3=19-$	$1+2+3+4+5=19-$	

$19-18+17-16+15-14+13-12=$

$19-(\frac{1}{2}\times 16)=$ $19-(\frac{1}{3}\times 9)-(\frac{1}{4}\times 12)=$

$\frac{12}{18}\times 15+\frac{7}{9}\times 9=$ $\frac{2}{3}\times 12+\frac{3}{7}\times 14=19-$

If you cannot do it, use the rods.

33. How many nines are there in nineteen? and how many left?

How many eights in nineteen? and how many left?

How many sevens in nineteen? and how many left?

How many sixes in nineteen? and how many left?

How many fives in nineteen? and how many left?

How many fours in nineteen? and how many left?

How many threes in nineteen? and how many left?

How many twos in nineteen? and how many left?

Since nineteen white rods cover the length nineteen, each white rod is called one nineteenth of that length and we write it $\frac{1}{19}$ of 19 or $\frac{1}{19}\times 19$.

What is $\frac{2}{19}\times 19$? and $\frac{8}{19}\times 19$? and $\frac{13}{19}\times 19$?

Compare $\frac{19}{19}\times 19$, $\frac{15}{15}\times 15$ and $\frac{13}{13}\times 13$.

Compare $\frac{17}{19}\times 19$, $\frac{17}{18}\times 18$ and $\frac{17}{17}\times 17$.

By how much is 19 bigger than 3×6? and than 5×3?

Study of 20

34. Two orange rods end to end make a length we call **twenty** which we write 20.

Make a pattern for 20 and write it down.

Complete the following in writing:

$2 \times 10=$ $2 \times 9+ \ =20$ $11+ \ =20$

$8+ \ =20$ $20-7=$ $20-12=$

$2 \times 5+ \ =20$ $3 \times 5+ \ =20$ $2 \times 7+ \ =20$

$12+6+ \ =20$ $13+\frac{1}{2} \times 14=$ $17+\frac{1}{3} \times 9=$

$20-\frac{2}{3} \times 9=$ $20-14+11=$ $20-\frac{1}{3} \times 18=$

$\frac{1}{2} \times 2+\frac{1}{2} \times 4+\frac{1}{2} \times 6+\frac{1}{2} \times 8+\frac{1}{2} \times 10=$

If you cannot do it, use the rods.

35. How many tens are there in twenty? and how much is left?

How many nines in twenty? and how much is left?

How many eights in twenty? and how much is left?

How many sevens in twenty? and how much is left?

How many sixes in twenty? and how much is left?

How many fives in twenty? and how much is left?

How many fours in twenty? and how much is left?

How many threes in twenty? and how much is left?

How many twos in twenty? and how much is left?

What is half of twenty or $\frac{1}{2} \times 20$?

What is a quarter of twenty or $\frac{1}{4} \times 20$?

What is a fifth of twenty or $\frac{1}{5} \times 20$?

What is a tenth of twenty or $\frac{1}{10} \times 20$?

What is $\frac{2}{4} \times 20$? and $\frac{1}{4} \times 20$?

What is $\frac{2}{5} \times 20$? and $\frac{3}{5} \times 20$? and $\frac{4}{5} \times 20$?

What is $\frac{3}{10} \times 20$? and $\frac{7}{10} \times 20$?

Compare $\frac{2}{10} \times 20$ and $\frac{1}{5} \times 20$.

Compare $\frac{4}{10} \times 20$ and $\frac{2}{5} \times 20$.

Compare $\frac{6}{10} \times 20$ and $\frac{3}{5} \times 20$.

Compare $\frac{8}{10} \times 20$ and $\frac{4}{5} \times 20$.

36. Since twenty white rods cover the length twenty, each white rod is called one twentieth of that length and we write it $\frac{1}{20}$ of 20 or $\frac{1}{20} \times 20$.

Compare $\frac{2}{20} \times 20$ and $\frac{1}{10} \times 20$.

Compare $\frac{4}{20} \times 20$, $\frac{2}{10} \times 20$ and $\frac{1}{5} \times 20$.

Compare $\frac{5}{20} \times 20$ and $\frac{1}{4} \times 20$.

Compare $\frac{6}{20} \times 20$ and $\frac{3}{10} \times 20$.

Compare $\frac{8}{20} \times 20$, $\frac{4}{10} \times 20$ and $\frac{2}{5} \times 20$.

Compare $\frac{10}{20} \times 20$, $\frac{5}{10} \times 20$ and $\frac{1}{2} \times 20$.

Compare $\frac{12}{20} \times 20$, $\frac{6}{10} \times 20$ and $\frac{3}{5} \times 20$.

Compare $\frac{14}{20} \times 20$ and $\frac{7}{10} \times 20$.

Compare $\frac{16}{20} \times 20$, $\frac{8}{10} \times 20$ and $\frac{4}{5} \times 20$.

Compare $\frac{18}{20} \times 20$ and $\frac{9}{10} \times 20$.

Compare $\frac{20}{20} \times 20$, $\frac{10}{10} \times 20$, $\frac{5}{5} \times 20$, $\frac{4}{4} \times 20$ and $\frac{2}{2} \times 20$.

37. What are the factors of 20?

Can you find in the wallchart the sign that has the colors of these factors? and in the pack of cards?

By how much is 20 bigger than 12? than 15? than 9?

Odd and even numbers

38. Which of the lengths from 1 to 20 can be made with red rods only?

Which cannot?

We have already called those which can be made **even numbers,** and the others **odd numbers.**

Write down the even numbers up to 20.

Write down the odd numbers up to 20.

Which of the following are even:

12, 17, 15, 20, 10, 5, 7, 13, 8, 11, 14, 16, 6, 3, 4, 1?

39. Give the factors of the following numbers:

12, 10, 20, 18, 6, 14, 16, 8, 4.

40. Numbers which have factors are called **composite.**

Give a few examples of composite numbers.

Numbers which have no factors other than one and themselves are called **prime.**

Give **all** the prime numbers up to 20.

Series

41. If we write

1, 2, 3, 4, 5, 6, 7, 8, 9, 10, 11, 12, 13, 14, 15, 16, 17, 18, 19, 20, we have put these numbers in **increasing order.**

If we write

20, 19, 18, 17, 16, 15, 14, 13, 12, 11, 10, 9, 8, 7, 6, 5, 4, 3, 2, 1, we have put them in **decreasing order.**

Put the following in decreasing order:

7, 20, 13, 8, 11, 10, 8, 19.

Put the following in decreasing order:

1, 19, 20, 12, 9, 13, 17, 14.

Put the answers to the following in increasing order:

3×4, 4×2, $7+9$, 5×1, $7+\frac{1}{2} \times 12$, $\frac{1}{3} \times 18+9$, 2×10.

Put the answers to the following in decreasing order:

$19-(\frac{1}{5} \times 10)$, $2 \times 7+1$, $20-\frac{1}{5} \times 15$, $18+\frac{1}{17} \times 17$, $12+\frac{2}{3} \times 6$.

Write in increasing order the answers to the following:

5×4	$2 \times 7+1$	$2 \times 4+3 \times 1$
$7+3 \times 3$	$3 \times 5+4$	$\frac{1}{3} \times 9+\frac{2}{5} \times 20$
$3 \times 6+1$	$2 \times 10-1$	$\frac{1}{2} \times 18+\frac{1}{2} \times 20$

If you cannot do it, use the rods.

Ordinal numbers

42. When numbers are put in order like this: 1, 2, 3, 4, 5, 6, 7, 8, 9, 10

1 is called **the first,**

2 is called **the second,**

3 is called **the third,**

4 is called **the fourth,**

5 is called **the fifth,**

6 is called **the sixth,**

7 is called **the seventh,**
8 is called **the eighth,**
9 is called **the ninth,**
10 is called **the tenth** in this series.

First, second, third, fourth, fifth, sixth, seventh, eighth, ninth and tenth when we use them in this way are called **ordinal** numbers.

In the following series

2, 3, 5, 7, 11, 13, 17, 19,

which is the first? the second? the third? the fourth? the fifth? the sixth? the seventh? the eighth?

And in this series

2, 4, 6, 8, 10, 12, 14, 16, 18, 20,

which is the tenth? the first? the second? the ninth? the third? the eighth? the fourth? the seventh? the fifth? the sixth?

43. Starting with 1, move up 2 by 2 in the series 1 to 20.
Which numbers do you get?
Starting with 19, move down 2 by 2.
Which numbers do you get?
Starting with 2, move up 2 by 2 in the series 1 to 20.
Which numbers do you get?
Starting with 20, move down 2 by 2.
Which numbers do you get?
Starting with 1, move up 3 by 3 in the series 1 to 20.
Which numbers do you get?
Starting with 20, move down 3 by 3.

Which numbers do you get?
Starting with 1, move up 4 by 4.
Write down your answers.
Starting with 20, move down 4 by 4.
Write down your answers.

44. From the series 1 to 20, how can we obtain the following series:

1, 3, 5, 7, 9, 11, 13, 15, 17, 19?

And how can we obtain this series:

2, 4, 6, 8, 10, 12, 14, 16, 18, 20?

And how can we obtain these series:

1, 4, 7, 10, 13, 16, 19

2, 6, 10, 14, 18

1, 6, 11, 16

20, 15, 10, 5?

Introducing zero

45. If we add two numbers together to form 10 we find

$$2+8=7+3=9+1=5+5=4+6$$

If we write 2+ $\quad$ =10 we find that what we need is 8.

If we write 7+ $\quad$ =10 we find that what we need is 3.

But if we write 10+ $\quad$ =10 we find that we need **nothing,** so we write 0 in the space and say **nought** or **zero.**

Thus we get

10+0=10, **ten plus zero is ten.**

But also $9+0=9$, $7+0=7$, $15+0=15$.

Can you complete these in writing:

$12+\ =12$ $\qquad$ $17+\ =17$ $\qquad$ $20+\ =20$

$2\times5+\ =10$ $\qquad$ $5\times3+\ =15$ $\qquad$ $3\times6+\ =18$?

We can also write:

$+3=10$ and find that what we need is 7.

$+11=13$ and find that what we need is 2.

But if we write:

$+3=3$ we find that we need **nothing** and we can again write the sign 0 in the space:

$0+3=3$, $0+7=7$, $0+11=11$.

Complete the following equations:

$+2\times6=12$ $\qquad\qquad$ $13+\ =2\times7-1$

$\frac{1}{2}\times18+\ =9$ $\qquad\qquad$ $+\frac{1}{3}\times12=4$

$+\frac{5}{6}\times12=2\times5$ $\qquad\qquad$ $+\frac{1}{7}\times(18-4)=2$

$7+8+0=$ $\qquad\qquad$ $4+0+5+10=$

$0+6+\frac{1}{2}\times18=$ $\qquad\qquad$ $17+3+0=$

$20+0-3=$ $\qquad\qquad$ $19+0-2\times6=$

Products

46. Complete the following equations:

$2\times1=$ $\qquad$ $2\times2=$ $\qquad$ $2\times3=$

$2\times4=$ $\qquad$ $2\times5=$ $\qquad$ $2\times6=$

$2\times7=$ $\qquad$ $2\times8=$ $\qquad$ $2\times9=$

$2\times10=$ $\qquad$ $\frac{1}{2}\times4=$ $\qquad$ $\frac{1}{2}\times6=$

$\frac{1}{2}\times2=$ $\qquad$ $\frac{1}{2}\times10=$ $\qquad$ $\frac{1}{2}\times12=$

$\frac{1}{2}\times8=$ $\qquad$ $\frac{1}{2}\times16=$ $\qquad$ $\frac{1}{2}\times18=$

$$\tfrac{1}{2} \times 14 = \qquad 3 \times 2 = \qquad 3 \times 3 =$$

$$\tfrac{1}{3} \times 20 = \qquad 3 \times 5 = \qquad 3 \times 6 =$$

$$3 \times 1 = \qquad \tfrac{1}{3} \times 6 = \qquad \tfrac{1}{3} \times 9 =$$

$$3 \times 4 = \qquad \tfrac{1}{3} \times 15 = \qquad \tfrac{1}{3} \times 18 =$$

$$\tfrac{1}{3} \times 3 = \qquad 4 \times 2 = \qquad 4 \times 3 =$$

$$\tfrac{1}{3} \times 12 = \qquad 4 \times 5 = \qquad \tfrac{1}{4} \times 12 =$$

$$4 \times 1 = \qquad \tfrac{1}{4} \times 8 = \qquad 5 \times 3 =$$

$$4 \times 4 = \qquad \tfrac{1}{4} \times 20 = \qquad \tfrac{1}{5} \times 15 =$$

$$\tfrac{1}{4} \times 4 = \qquad 5 \times 2 = \qquad 6 \times 3 =$$

$$\tfrac{1}{4} \times 16 = \qquad \tfrac{1}{5} \times 10 = \qquad \tfrac{1}{6} \times 18 =$$

$$5 \times 1 = \qquad 6 \times 2 = \qquad 10 \times 2 =$$

$$5 \times 4 = \qquad \tfrac{1}{6} \times 12 = \qquad \tfrac{1}{10} \times 20 =$$

$$\tfrac{1}{5} \times 5 = \qquad 7 \times 2 = \qquad 8 \times 1 =$$

$$\tfrac{1}{5} \times 20 = \qquad \tfrac{1}{7} \times 14 = \qquad \tfrac{1}{8} \times 8 =$$

$$6 \times 1 = \qquad 8 \times 2 = \qquad 9 \times 1 =$$

$$\tfrac{1}{6} \times 6 = \qquad \tfrac{1}{8} \times 16 = \qquad \tfrac{1}{9} \times 9 =$$

$$7 \times 1 = \qquad 9 \times 2 = \qquad 10 \times 1 =$$

$$\tfrac{1}{7} \times 7 = \qquad \tfrac{1}{9} \times 18 = \qquad \tfrac{1}{10} \times 10 =$$

47. Write as many products as you can for the following numbers:

4, 6, 8, 9, 10, 12, 14, 15, 16, 18, 20.

Find them on the wallchart.

Find them in the pack of cards.

Take from the bag the counters which show the above numbers and mix them up in another bag. With three or six other pupils, play the game of lotto.

Exchange cards and play the game again.
With one other pupil play the following game:

> Draw one counter each from your new bag.
> The one who draws the bigger number takes
> the other as well, until all the counters are
> used up.

Repeat this game, this time using the cards which
show the products up to 20.

Go on playing as long as you like, writing down
the numbers you win and those you lose.

Short division

48. We shall now write some of the lines of
our patterns in a new way, and we shall call
them **short divisions.**

When we try to make a length by using rods of
one color only, we find that sometimes we can
do it and sometimes we cannot.

When we can, we get the factors of the particular
number. But prime numbers have no factors
other than themselves and one, so that we can
never complete their lengths with rods of one
color, apart from the white.

We know how to answer the following questions:
How many 8's in 19?
How many 5's in 12?
How many 4's in 15?
How many 6's in 20?

The answers are: 2 and 3 left; 2 and 2 left;
3 and 3 left; 3 and 2 left.

We can write:

$$19 = 2 \times 8 + 3 \qquad 12 = 2 \times 5 + 2$$
$$15 = 3 \times 4 + 3 \qquad 20 = 3 \times 6 + 2$$

Instead of asking how many 8's there are in 19 we shall write $19 \div 8$ and read it as 19 **divided** by 8, and write the answer

$19 \div 8 = 2$ **remainder** 3.

Read the following:

$12 \div 5 = 2$ remainder 2.

$15 \div 4 = 3$ remainder 3.

$20 \div 6 = 3$ remainder 2.

Make the pattern of 17, trying to use only one color in each line, and write down the answers to:

$17 \div 2 =$	$17 \div 3 =$	$17 \div 4 =$
$17 \div 5 =$	$17 \div 6 =$	$17 \div 7 =$
$17 \div 8 =$		

49. Give the answers to

$7 \div 2 =$	$7 \div 3 =$	$7 \div 4 =$
$7 \div 5 =$	$7 \div 6 =$	
$8 \div 3 =$	$8 \div 5 =$	$8 \div 6 =$
$8 \div 7 =$		
$9 \div 2 =$	$9 \div 4 =$	$9 \div 5 =$
$9 \div 6 =$	$9 \div 7 =$	$9 \div 8 =$
$10 \div 3 =$	$10 \div 4 =$	$10 \div 6 =$
$10 \div 7 =$	$10 \div 8 =$	$10 \div 9 =$
$11 \div 2 =$	$11 \div 3 =$	$11 \div 4 =$
$11 \div 5 =$	$11 \div 6 =$	$11 \div 7 =$

$11 \div 8 =$	$11 \div 9 =$	$11 \div 10 =$
$12 \div 5 =$	$12 \div 7 =$	$12 \div 8 =$
$12 \div 9 =$	$12 \div 10 =$	$12 \div 11 =$

50. Give the answers to

$13 \div 2 =$	$13 \div 3 =$	$13 \div 4 =$
$13 \div 5 =$	$13 \div 6 =$	$13 \div 7 =$
$13 \div 8 =$	$13 \div 9 =$	$13 \div 10 =$
$13 \div 11 =$	$13 \div 12 =$	
$14 \div 3 =$	$14 \div 4 =$	$14 \div 5 =$
$14 \div 6 =$	$14 \div 8 =$	$14 \div 9 =$
$14 \div 10 =$	$14 \div 11 =$	$14 \div 12 =$
$14 \div 13 =$		
$15 \div 2 =$	$15 \div 4 =$	$15 \div 6 =$
$15 \div 7 =$	$15 \div 8 =$	$15 \div 9 =$
$15 \div 10 =$	$15 \div 11 =$	$15 \div 12 =$
$15 \div 13 =$	$15 \div 14 =$	
$16 \div 3 =$	$16 \div 5 =$	$16 \div 6 =$
$16 \div 7 =$	$16 \div 9 =$	$16 \div 10 =$
$16 \div 11 =$	$16 \div 12 =$	$16 \div 13 =$
$16 \div 14 =$	$16 \div 15 =$	

51. Give the answers to

$17 \div 9 =$	$17 \div 10 =$	$17 \div 11 =$
$17 \div 12 =$	$17 \div 13 =$	$17 \div 14 =$
$17 \div 15 =$	$17 \div 16 =$	
$18 \div 4 =$	$18 \div 5 =$	$18 \div 7 =$
$18 \div 8 =$	$18 \div 10 =$	$18 \div 11 =$

$18 \div 12 =$	$18 \div 13 =$	$18 \div 14 =$
$18 \div 15 =$	$18 \div 16 =$	$18 \div 17 =$
$19 \div 2 =$	$19 \div 3 =$	$19 \div 4 =$
$19 \div 5 =$	$19 \div 6 =$	$19 \div 7 =$
$19 \div 8 =$	$19 \div 9 =$	$19 \div 10 =$
$19 \div 11 =$	$19 \div 12 =$	$19 \div 13 =$
$19 \div 14 =$	$19 \div 15 =$	$19 \div 16 =$
$19 \div 17 =$	$19 \div 18 =$	
$20 \div 3 =$	$20 \div 6 =$	$20 \div 7 =$
$20 \div 8 =$	$20 \div 9 =$	$20 \div 11 =$
$20 \div 12 =$	$20 \div 13 =$	$20 \div 14 =$
$20 \div 15 =$	$20 \div 16 =$	$20 \div 17 =$
$20 \div 18 =$	$20 \div 19 =$	

52. When there is no remainder, as in $18 \div 6$ or $16 \div 4$, we can use either the division sign $\div$ or the line for fractions $\frac{18}{6}$ or $\frac{16}{4}$, and write

$$\frac{18}{6} = 3 \text{ or } \frac{16}{4} = 4.$$

Complete the following in writing:

$\frac{15}{3} =$	$20 \div 4 =$	$\frac{20}{5} =$	$\frac{12}{4} =$
$12 \div 3 =$	$\frac{15}{5} =$	$15 \div 3 =$	$\frac{14}{7} =$
$10 \div 5 =$	$14 \div 2 =$	$\frac{20}{4} =$	$20 \div 5 =$